Ingrid

I wanted you to get a copy of this & hope you enjoy the stories & insight.

Your encouragement as I discussed this project is much appreciated

Enjoy !

Your very dear friend

By God, if I Were in Charge...

A book about experiences in the Pipeline Industry

By God, if I Were in Charge...

A book about experiences in the Pipeline Industry

 JTRAIN, INC.

By God, if I Were in Charge … a book about experiences in the pipeline industry

Copyright © 2020 JTrain, Inc. All rights reserved. This publication, and parts thereof, may not be reproduced, stored, shared or transmitted in any manner without written permission from the publishers, JTrain, Inc.

Library of Congress Control Number 2019915332
ISBN 978-0-9906-7008-7

Published by

 JTRAIN, INC.

5819 Pinelake Crossing Drive, Spring, TX 77379, USA

Distributed by
Clarion Technical Publishers, 3401 Louisiana Street, Suite 110, Houston, TX 77002, USA
T: +1 713 521 5929 | e: info@clarion.org

A Concept Inspired by Jerry Rau

Contents

Foreword

George Tenley, Past President of PRCI

This is a book about the pipeline industry. An industry that builds, manages, and operates a vast energy network, sometimes called "the Nation's energy lifelines." It is an industry that enabled the vast post-World War II economic resurgence across all aspects of American life. It is an industry that has brought to fruition numerous technological advances from higher grade steels, and the accompanying welding processes, to remote sensing and monitoring, to sophisticated corrosion control techniques. It is an industry that is subject to thorough legislative and regulatory scrutiny, and one that operates under a broad set of consensus industry standards.

But, as revealed in the chapters that follow, it is, perhaps more importantly, an industry that has been sustained and improved by some of the world's most competent engineers, technicians, and researchers. However, not unlike other major industrial components, a larger percentage of these professionals are leaving the industry than are joining it. Given this reality, and the critical role of the pipeline industry for the foreseeable future, the greatest operating challenge faced by the pipeline industry is how best to transfer this vast wellspring of knowledge – and wisdom – to the generations that follow. And, in so doing, to assure that we continually develop new leaders to optimize the skills the incoming generations will bring to the endeavor.

So, this book is not an expose or a book of gripes about the pipeline industry. It is a book about people who have a great passion for the industry and who have spent most, if not all, of their professional lives making it better, safer, and more sustainable. It is about people who have seen a great deal of change, gained experience and strived for continual improvement. In the pages that follow, these professionals will share that knowledge with those who follow. One of the underlying objectives of this book is to present improvement opportunities - in science, operations, standards and regulations - without the constraints of limited resources and the bureaucracies pipeline professionals must often endure. However, these improvements can be most successfully realized in a timely and thorough manner through a knowledge transfer paradigm that is grounded in creative approaches to education.

Moreover, this book is not a technical report nor is it a textbook. It is a narrative from the people who have been heavily involved in the pipeline industry for decades. Each chapter describes an outcome of that knowledge gained by performing research, writing standards and procedures, influencing regulations, and operating pipelines.

The opinions of the authors are based on all of that accumulated knowledge. Because of that, another key objective is to make the book readable. For the most part it is written in the first person. We want the readers to hear what the author is saying. Too often detailed references become distracting to the central message, and so we have strived to keep them to a minimum. The way the author has chosen to present his or her perspective is unique to the author, so you will read chapters that are almost conversational, while others are more technical. This merely reflects the dynamic, diverse nature of these highly talented, committed, and experienced professionals.

Certainly, based on your own experience in the industry, or perhaps your professional biases, you may challenge the opinions presented in this book. But, bear in mind, those opinions are well-founded and are based on the authors' knowledge and experience. Whether you endorse and accept the perspectives presented here, I believe you will find that important knowledge is being transferred to you, and you can use to it support your own growth in an industry on which we all depend so heavily.

George W. Tenley
Formerly, Associate Administrator for Pipeline Safety, Pipeline and Hazardous Materials Administration (Research and Special Programs Administration), U.S, Department of Transportation; 1989 - 1995

Formerly, President, Pipeline Research Council International, Inc.; 1999 - 2010

About the authors

First of all, many thanks to each of the authors for their commitment, time, and most of all, insight.

Those who have worked with me in PRCI know most of my best work was done in "My Office" after hours. It was there that I learned so much about the true nature of the mechanisms that are threats to pipeline steel, how research increases our knowledge about those threats and their prevention, and, most important, the commitment of the researchers and operators to manage them. In those long hours at "My Office" we developed close relationships and discussed a myriad of topics, not necessarily all related to pipeline research.

I've worked with **Dave Johnson** (**Dr. Dave**) for many years, first through trade groups and standards writing organizations. Then we worked together at Cross Country Pipeline / Southern Union / Panhandle Energy / Energy Transfer. Dr. Dave is well known for his love of rock and roll music and sharp wit. He does love a good argument (probably a bad one as well).

Dr. Keith Leewis has a wide and varied career. As he would say, he's just a dumbass welder. But, he has taken that knowledge and firsthand experience and contributed mightily to the pipeline world and pipeline integrity in particular. A true and dear friend. Be careful of his wit as well, as he will pun you out of your mind.

I first met **Bill Amend** when he was with SoCalGas. He was involved in PRCI and we found ourselves in many conversations about the state of the Industry and where it needed to go. He was the first of the "volunteers" I contacted to respond. His two chapters surely let his passion about our Industry shine through.

The old Panhandle Eastern Pipeline Company (PEPL) contributed mightily to the Industry over the years and was a founding member of PRCI. PEPL was heavily involved and understood how critical it was to participate, be seen and help drive the direction. **Bill Bruce** is an old Panhandler just like me. Our careers didn't overlap there, but he left quite a legacy. The mutual bond of that company has extended over many years. He is and always will be my go-to guy for anything welding. Of course, being retired / retired, I don't run into many welding problems anymore!

Dr. Brian Leis and I go back many years. He joined me in "My Office" many times, and we've had quite the lively conversations about how best to attack a research project. He is a perfectionist. He has provided some of the largest leaps in technology to our industry over the years. We are still expanding on these building blocks today.

Shawn Laughlin is an accomplished engineer, as you will become acutely aware of when you read his chapter. But, I came to know him best as an entrepreneur providing repair solutions. We've had a few lively discussions regarding non-steel sleeves for repair. I had the great fortune to co-author a paper with him on that very subject. It was one of the most enjoyable presentations I've ever had.

My relationship with **Geoff Foreman** began when his company joined as an Associate Member in PRCI. His knowledge of the ILI world and its origins is unparalleled. His contribution to that part of our Industry was huge. When he spoke at a PRCI meeting, everyone paid attention! The good news is he has returned to his home in England, and the bad news I don't get to see his as often. Our trips around the golf course have become less frequent.

Of all the authors, I've known **Mike Gloven** for the shortest time. We met through a mutual business acquaintance. I am very pleased he accepted the invitation to contribute a chapter. It is well written and very true to intent of the book.

A great deal of thanks is owed to **George Tenley** as special editor. His editing kept the contents readable and true to the commitment of this book. Without his efforts this book would not have happened. More importantly, George gave me the passion for pipeline research and a greater understanding of the family of pipeline professionals. Special thanks to George for writing the perfect Foreword for this book.

And, of course, love and appreciation to **Jane Rau** my intelligent, beautiful, gracious and talented wife, and demanding editor. She's put up with me for 43 years. I could never have imagined that our professional lives would have crossed paths. I am very grateful they did.

Jerry F Rau
Chief Engineer. Jtrain – Inc.
Retired / Retired

How regulations and standards help and get in the way

Jerry F. Rau (retired/retired)

> *I'd have science teach us what we don't know, write*
> *standards based on the best science, and adopt*
> *necessary regulations based on those standards.*

How did I get here?

Who goes to engineering school in 1970 to become a pipeline engineer? It's unlikely that anyone in my college class of 1970 at Marquette University, or anywhere else for that matter, was studying to become a pipeline engineer. I'm not sure that I was even aware there was a network of pipelines across the country. All I knew was I wanted to become a mechanical engineer, even though I wasn't exactly sure what knowledge I would need and to what practical application my degree could be applied. I did know that "Civvies" and "Double E's" were beneath our contempt and could only be trusted to change the channel on the TV in the student lounge or build concrete canoes!

My journey began in 1974 when I graduated with a BSME. The Vietnam war was winding down, the economy was in a deep recession and jobs were scarce. I was broke and still living at home. My dad worked for the telephone company and he had a friend that worked for Wisconsin Gas Company. So it came to be that, without any prep work or forethought, I joined the pipeline industry.

In those days there was an Engineer in Training (EIT) program at the gas company. New engineers were given two months to get a taste of the different aspects of gas utility operations and shadow workers from various departments. At the end of the EIT, whatever openings existed for engineers were filled. I don't recall exactly, but I think there were two or three of us that year. I do remember there were openings in the design department, research department and corrosion control. At the time, the company was at the forefront of introducing plastic pipe for gas mains and services. The chief engineer in the research group was highly regarded in that field. Seemed pretty interesting to me. So, of course, I was offered the position of cathodic protection engineer in the corrosion control group! As the saying goes, here is the rest of the story.

What did I learn along the way?

The way we used to learn was by advice from subject matter experts (SMEs), but they weren't called that back then. The assumption was they were smart, knew how and what to do and "had seen it all." Some of them had and some of them hadn't. Some were willing to share, some not so much. But, in the end it was my responsibility, or so I thought, to apply the lessons and directions given to me. Then it was expected that I would verify those applications by referring to standards, research reports and, of course, the regulations. We learned by watching and hopefully asking the right questions along the way. Children should be seen and not heard.

I'd suggest that I progressed in my career the right way. Starting off at a natural gas utility gave me lots of fundamentals. Then I was off to Saudi Arabia, working in production and pipelines where I started as a pipeline maintenance engineer and then transferred back into the CP world as a Corrosion Engineer. In contrast to the natural gas utility world, everything in Saudi was big including the budgets. It was a great experience culturally as well as technically. I was exposed to large pipeline projects, welding, pipeline construction and pipeline maintenance. This was followed by a brief stint with a CP consultancy. That job provided me perspective from the other side of the desk. The owner warned me that when you enter the room with a client you are considered the dumbest and least trustworthy person in the room. You have to earn the client's respect. I like to think I was able to do that, from the early days up through my most recent endeavors.

The bulk of my career following my Saudi Arabian sojourn was spent with a natural gas transmission company based in Houston. In my various roles I was exposed to many aspects of the energy pipeline business, including work in operations, in the field, in corporate headquarters and as a consultant. It is those experiences that have enlightened my viewpoint on how things are done and how they *should* be done.

As with most engineers, I believe technology and the development of new technology are exciting. I've had the opportunity to work closely with, and help direct, R&D efforts through Pipeline Research Council International (PRCI). I've worked with Standard Writing Organization (SWOs) in developing industry standards and with those same organizations and trade groups in advocating for changes to federal regulations. I've worked with state and federal regulators, but mostly federal. I've had to defend the company's position after an incident or when the company was alleged of not following the rules.

I've been working in the pipeline Industry for most of my 44-year career. We all know that longevity doesn't necessarily bring worthwhile experience or competence. The engineer with 30 years of experience – 1 year 30 times – comes to mind. You're never too old to gain experience.

Is it hard to retire? Retirement for many pipeline professionals is not a date or singularity but rather a continuum. I routinely say I'm retired/retired and that when I reach the third "retired," I will stop working completely. I've heard it put this way: "For every 10 years of service add 1.5 years to the transition to full retirement."

Many things have changed, yet sadly many things have remained the same. But that is what this chapter is about: some insights and maybe even some solutions!

Pipe is pipe, right?

What would the pipeline industry look like without federal regulations? An intriguing and very controversial topic. But is it a stretch? Would we be better off "self-regulated?" Could we be self- regulated? Regulations were not always a foregone conclusion. Engineering standards have existed for hundreds of years, but pipeline standards like B31 were later to the game. In 1926, the American Standards Association initiated Project B31 to develop a piping code. The American Society of Mechanical Engineers (ASME) was the sole administrative sponsor. The first publication of this document, *American Tentative Standard Code for Pressure Piping*, was in 1935. From 1942 through 1955 the Code was published as the *American Standard Code for Pressure Piping*, ASA B31.1. It was composed of separate sections for different industries. These sections were split off starting in 1955 with *Gas Transmission and Distribution Piping Systems* ASA B31.8, ASA B31.3, *Petroleum Refinery Piping Code*, was first published in 1959. API 1104 for pipeline welding was first published in about 1949.

It is arguable that the existing standards of the time provided sufficient guidance for operators to maintain their pipelines safely. Of course, history would reveal that incidents occurred and R&D was not sufficiently robust, resulting in a demand from an anxious public for more guidance and control. This reaction to accidents has come to be a defining element in the evolution of legislation and regulation addressing pipeline safety.

Accordingly, CFR Part 192 was introduced in 1970 to implement the Natural Gas Pipeline Safety Act of 1968. Part 195 was adopted later under the Hazardous Liquid Pipeline Safety Act of 1979.

So, it is reasonable to observe that regulations aren't going away; but, are they promulgated, written, reviewed and enforced as effectively as possible? Why are there different regulations for gas versus hazardous liquids? Why are there fewer performance regulations and more prescriptive regulations? Why should regulators care how the industry maintains safe conditions, as long as they do it successfully? Couldn't the regulations stand on a very simple set of directives: don't hurt anybody, don't cause property or environmental damage, and follow the appropriate industry standards? Shouldn't we leave the "how to" to the standards and use very large penalties for failing to meet those basic criteria of "do no harm?"

Pipe is pipe right? The current regulations, for the most part, only consider hoop stress in the design equations. I'll leave that discussion for others to consider or for another time. Pipe doesn't know and pretty much doesn't care what is being transported, as long as the hoop stress from the pressure of the product is below its applicable strength. When you look at the life cycle of a pipeline – Design, Construction, Commissioning, Operations, Maintenance and Decommissioning – most of these functions can be treated as relating to "just pipe." Now don't get all riled up. I know that according to current regulations and Industry standards the product that's in the pipe impacts the design and other aspects. But for every aspect of each part of the design and construction it doesn't need to be that way.

Let's look at the life cycle and how to design, construct and maintain a pipeline if we could start over. Wouldn't you (I would) craft a standard that starts with the most generic aspects of a natural gas or hazardous liquid pipeline and then proceed to the more specific, then most specific aspects? I understand there are complex problems of design with complex solutions, but designing a pipeline is not one of those. The inherent strength of the material, steel in most cases, is well established*. We know how it is manufactured, tested at the mill and tested on the construction site. We've been doing it for decades and, arguably, very successfully. Let's treat all pipe the same in the design for strength with appropriate safety factors for natural gas and hazardous liquid pipelines.

The process of designing, constructing operating and maintaining pipelines could be vastly simplified by combining the current indus-

---

* "Steel pipe metallurgy continues to evolve leading to new problems. Example: high-strength pipe with modern compositions is now subject to weld HAZ softening, which is almost polar opposite to vintage HAZ behavior where we were worried more about high hardness and hydrogen cracking." In email from Bill Amend.

try standards for natural gas and hazardous liquid pipelines and then redoing Parts 192 and 195 to reflect those changes. The process of executing against the standards, confirming compliance and enforcing the regulations would eliminate a great deal of confusion and verify a much higher level of consistency. I would bet the "public" would be for it and support the effort and results.

In the past for the most part there were Natural Gas Operators and Hazardous Liquids Operators. Their process and procedures (O&M manuals, SOPs) were fitted for operating those specific types of assets. The personnel were specifically trained and qualified for the Natural gas or Hazardous Liquid environment. Now, many operators in North America and around the world operate natural gas and hazardous liquid assets concurrently. They must have process and procedures for each specific standard and regulation that pertain to the requirements of Natural Gas (192) and Hazardous liquid (195). Sometimes the same personnel operate pipelines under both cases. Certainly there can be confusion and duplication. Let's look at a few examples of differences in Parts 192 and 195. Below are some excerpts from the corrosion control requirements in 192.467 and 195.575.

§192.467 External corrosion control: Electrical isolation. 1)

"(a) Each buried or submerged pipeline must be electrically isolated from other underground metallic structures, unless the pipeline and the other structures are electrically interconnected and cathodically protected as a single unit.

(b) One or more insulating devices must be installed where electrical isolation of a portion of a pipeline is necessary to facilitate the application of corrosion control.

(c) Except for unprotected copper inserted in ferrous pipe, each pipeline must be electrically isolated from metallic casings that are a part of the underground system. However, if isolation is not achieved because it is impractical, other measures must be taken to minimize corrosion of the pipeline inside the casing.

(d) Inspection and electrical tests must be made to assure that electrical isolation is adequate.

(e) An insulating device may not be installed in an area where a combustible atmosphere is anticipated unless precautions are taken to prevent arcing.

(f) Where a pipeline is located in close proximity to electrical transmission tower footings, ground cables or counterpoise, or in other areas where fault currents or unusual risk of lightning may be anticipated, it must be provided with protection against damage due to fault currents or lightning, and protective measures must also be taken at insulating devices."

§195.575 Which facilities must I electrically isolate and what inspections, tests, and safeguards are required?

"(a) You must electrically isolate each buried or submerged pipeline from other metallic structures, unless you electrically interconnect and cathodically protect the pipeline and the other structures as a single unit.

(b) You must install one or more insulating devices where electrical isolation of a portion of a pipeline is necessary to facilitate the application of corrosion control.

(c) You must inspect and electrically test each electrical isolation to assure the isolation is adequate.

(d) If you install an insulating device in an area where a combustible atmosphere is reasonable to foresee, you must take precautions to prevent arcing.

(e) If a pipeline is in close proximity to electrical transmission tower footings, ground cables, or counterpoise, or in other areas where it is reasonable to foresee fault currents or an unusual risk of lightning, you must protect the pipeline against damage from fault currents or lightning and take protective measures at insulating devices."

Why do we have to say it twice with the potential for different interpretations and misapplication?

The following is an excerpt from Part 192 that describes the requirements to apply cathodic protection. There is no equivalent wording in part 195, nor is the word "remedial" used in any context in part 195.

§192.483 Remedial measures: General. 2)

"(a) Each segment of metallic pipe that replaces pipe removed from a buried or submerged pipeline because of external corrosion must have a properly prepared surface and must be provided with an external protective coating that meets the requirements of §192.461.

(b) Each segment of metallic pipe that replaces pipe removed from a buried or submerged pipeline because of external corrosion must be cathodically protected in accordance with this subpart.

(c) Except for cast iron or ductile iron pipe, each segment of buried or submerged pipe that is required to be repaired because of external corrosion must be cathodically protected in accordance with this subpart."

For a very important aspect of corrosion control, only one of the regulations describes how remedial action must be performed, and it is certainly confusing in its use of the word "remedial." How much extra time, resources, paperwork and confusion are a result of the status quo? I suggest that a great reduction in effort would be the result. The public would benefit from more transparency, more consistency and less confusion.

Let's look at the role of R&D in establishing and confirming pipeline safety. Why is research (science) so important? Simply put, if regulations are not based on the most recent science, pipeline safety and the public good are compromised. Although regulations have been deemed necessary, history shows they are not sufficient to embody all that goes into the operation of a pipeline, or a pipeline system.

We can make regulations and the regulatory process better by turning the existing paradigm upside down.

The way it is now

Incident ⟹ Regulation ⟹ Standard ⟹ Research

The way it should be

Research ⟹ Standard ⟹ Regulation? ⟹ Incident Prevented?

High-profile Incidents, no matter how significant, influence regulators' and pipeline operators' thinking. A short-term response, such as PHMSA's Corrective Action Orders, carries over to all pipelines through PHMSA integrated inspections, IM program reviews and other regulatory mandates. The longer-term response is, of course, NTSB reports and recommendations, which often lead to new legislation and rulemaking. In general terms, the current reliance on reaction leads to a "good, bad, and ugly" reality, namely -

- *Good* – can lead to a focus on events that impact industry broadly or are identified as emerging topics;
- *Bad* - can divert resources from other important work; and,
- *Ugly* - may not be a significant industry concern/emerging issue or it may be a one-off that has little relevance to most operators

It is likely that one incident does not make the event "significant" relative to the overall industry. Cooperation among regulators, operators, the research community and service providers is required to re-define the current process. To become predictive, the pipeline industry must continually perform research to address the reality that "we don't know what we don't know." As we gain answers to that reality, we should use that knowledge to formulate new Industry standards. Then, let the Industry standards drive the need for new regulations due to changes in technology or process solutions.

So, what's the answer? I didn't say it would be easy. Is it worth the effort? It could take a long time and there are toes to be stepped on and empires to be challenged. But isn't that exactly the philosophy of the Millennial Generation? Are the millennials in industry, science, and government willing to apply their talents to this effort, and are their leaders willing to support them? I leave it up to the reader.

It's about the process, right?

The pursuit of excellence under a quality management system (QMS) is about performance, consistency and compliance. If you do the first two and have clearly established performance goals, compliance will be the result. In some form or fashion, every company has a QMS which is used to verify that the right person does the right job in the right place at the right time with the right results. The QMS is overarching in terms of what the company expects from each person and process. Pipeline Safety Management Systems (PSMS) are being implemented by many companies and are well defined in the API standard 1173. The Integrity Management (IM) process is a subset of PSMS and provides details on risk assessment and risk management of the pipeline assets. The end result is consistency and excellence of the People, Process, Product and Pipe.

Quality Management Systems

Operators have traditionally been very good at data management, but maybe not so good at process management. All pipeline operators have or are working toward a PSMS. Here's an analogy from a good friend: PSMS is like the man who claims to have a race car. His friends have never seen it or heard of any results, so they question him. How fast is it? What are typical lap times? How many races has it won? He explains that the engine is at the machine shop on a dyno. The chassis is at the garage, the suspension, tires and wheels at the brake shop, the electronics at the electrical shop and the driver and crew are racing a dragster in California. All the pieces are there, so surely it is a race car!

Procedures are necessary and, in many cases, required. They are used to describe the step-by-step activities required to perform a task (maintain a valve, perform a close interval survey, etc.). It is necessary to document the results of those activities (i.e., valve was greased on 1/1/2009). Processes describe the actions taken (or not taken) when performing the procedures and documenting the decisions.

The difference between process and procedures? Consider - You dig up a regulated pipeline and find a steel repair sleeve at that location. What can you conclude? First of all, there were procedures on sleeve selection, excavation and backfill, installation and welding. There is a high probability that these procedures were followed and the prescribed documentation completed and stored. But, is there documentation of the process? Why is the sleeve there? What led to the conclusion a sleeve was necessary? What, if any, alternatives were considered, and what did they learn after the process was completed?

The next step in integrity management, a subset of pipeline safety management, is the establishment of better metrics. Performance management naturally leads to better process management. Performance management is managing efforts to verify the correct results. You can manage efforts and thereby affect results, but you cannot manage results, you can only verify them. The expectation is that Process Management will drive specific actions in specific areas to address specific problems based on risk prioritization.

Performance measurements are those measures that verify objectives have been met. You must establish Key Performance Indicators (KPI) which are both Leading Indicators (measurement of efforts) and Lagging Indicators (measurement of results). The establishment of performance measures is relative to the objective. What in some cases has been considered a lagging indicator may in fact be a leading indicator if the objective was safety vs. plan implementation. Measurement of leading indicators demonstrates performance to determine if the right efforts are being made to properly affect the results. The same measures may be leading for performance, but lagging for compliance. In a performance environment, leading indicators measure the efforts to prevent corrosion, locate corrosion, and repair corrosion prior to failure. A lagging indicator is metal loss caused by corrosion, which may be the root cause of anomalies, failures, incidents, damages and loss of containment.

How do we confirm compliance? Compliance auditing is regularly done with question sets that generate binary answers. The answer will either be that the auditee is in compliance or out of compliance with a specific requirement. This approach can answer many questions but does not address why the auditee is in or out of compliance and, if out of compliance, what went wrong and what should be done to bring the organization into compliance.

A better approach to auditing regulatory compliance, rather than simply asking and answering PHMSA protocol questions, is to look at the process by which your organization manages system integrity and reliability. The processes and how you manage them are not random. They are well prescribed by industry standards and your company's experience and best practices. The experience and use of best practices gained from many years of operations are extremely valuable as well. When you map your processes and then determine if you have accomplished safety, reliability and integrity, compliance will follow. Don't map your processes to the regulations. Map the regulations to the structures for your process flow.

This approach will assist you in determining if there are any gaps in your processes and process management. The links to compliance requirements can then be easily matched to what you do, which may be above and beyond the requirements of the regulations. That is where you want to be, as the regulatory requirements are simply the starting point for a safe, reliable system with the level of integrity your organization desires.

The basic, conventional outline of a process for the "how" an organization can manage compliance is as follows:

- Know what the applicable requirements are down to individual compliance tasks.
- Document the individual compliance tasks.
- Identify the roles of the personnel responsible for each compliance task.
- Communicate that responsibility to those personnel and train them on the compliance task.
- Document instructions for how to do the task, and make them available to the responsible person.

- Identify the records to be used to demonstrate the task was done or compliance was achieved.
- Have a reporting/tracking process for when compliance was not achieved.
- Design and implement a self-assessment procedure to check compliance and the compliance process.
- Have clear compliance performance indicators and measure the performance against the indicators. Take action to improve performance as necessary.

We need to embrace a different strategy and utilize a technical basis for standards and regulations where application of enhanced technology is the key to success. The goal of integrity management should be performance rather than compliance. Compliance is necessary, but not sufficient. On top of compliance is the application of best (or at least common) practices. Company specific operational needs have to be considered. If there are conflicts, the reasons a specific path was chosen need to be documented and shown be technically defensible. Process management supports issue resolution, decision-making and communication.

Break down the silos and tunnels, and get all the pieces working effectively together. Manage the outcomes with more detailed metrics. Learn the lessons and share them with all parts of the organization. Apply the science and technology. Actively engage in R&D. Find out what you don't know and become more predictive. Don't assume it's all in place. Survey the organization from side to side and top to bottom.

Why can't we all get along?

We would be better off if we ALL could get along, right? Why do we resist transparency and sharing? *We* can get along better, where "getting along" includes information sharing, working collaboratively on standards, research, and regulations, and being ready and willing to listen to the informed ideas of those we serve and to whom we are responsible.

In the context of pipeline safety, the "We" are the company, the Industry and the public (external stakeholders; e.g., the residents along our rights of way and the elected and appointed government officials who represent them). When we talked about process management, we discussed how important commitment and communication are. In other words, we need to get along.

There are company goals: safety, reliability and profitability. Profit is not a dirty word. Companies need to be profitable to be able to achieve the first two goals. Highly Reliable Organizations (HRO) recognize that safety and reliability are both critical aspects of a company's objectives - you can be highly reliable and very safe at the same time. Sometimes, due to resource constraints, managing in chaos, or in an emergency, these objectives can be temporarily opposed. Flight operations on an aircraft carrier are very complex, which have as their goals the highest reliability and safety achievable. In peacetime, normal operations, this is achieved and safety stand-downs will occur and aircraft taken out of service to meet scheduled maintenance requirements. However, in time of war, reliability becomes paramount. All aircraft need to fly as often as possible, even at the expense of deferring maintenance. I've obviously simplified the example and do not mean that safety is jeopardized; but, priorities can and do shift. Even HROs will prioritize and shift priorities between safety and reliability from time to time. This is a reality pipeline professionals face every day. When organization A sets the budget priorities, does organization B fully comprehend the consequence (long- and short-term) of cancelling a project or reducing its scope? Commitment and communication help reinforce the goals and verify everyone is on the same page.

Organizational culture sets the stage for clear goals, well-established objectives and a path everyone in the organization can follow and support. In terms of commitment and communication, silos and tunnels are one of the main obstacles for effective implementation. Not everyone starts on the same page or stays on the same page. We know in our organization ALL procedures are in place. They are well written, provide sufficient detail, incorporate industry best practices, document the process and the results and assist in verifying compliance (heavy sarcasm intended). Right? We need to get along! Everyone in the organization from top to bottom (CEO to boots on the ground) and across (divisions and departments) need to get along. It is critical to have clear definitions of who is responsible, accountable and has the authority for a specific decision. Without that clarity, it can lead to unqualified people making technical decisions that may be contrary to SME inputs. This can happen when unqualified people have a level of authority without the commensurate and appropriate levels of accountability.

We are a competitive Industry, and there are laws that restrict what we can discuss and share. But when it comes to public safety, shouldn't we share our lessons learned and experiences? Shouldn't we be open and honest and share all the details? We already doing that, right? We have API, NACE, ASME, INGAA, PRCI and other organizations that hold a multitude of conferences and workshops. Are these organizations well connected and communicating effectively between each other? Do the organizations stick to their mission statements? Advocacy groups should stick to advocacy, standard writing organizations should only write standards and research organizations should stay away from advocacy. We can get along better. A better outcome is obtained when the company volunteers are held accountable and corporate officials support their volunteers. The accountability is realized when the people who represent an operator for any of these organizations communicate with management, verify with management what the company message and direction is, verify not only commitment to the organization but consistency in the message.

A great deal of information is shared at every one of these conferences. Are we transparent enough, or are we too afraid of loss of intellectual property and competitive advantage? Why are most conferences dominated by service providers and not by papers written by operators? We can get along better. Operators verify with their participants in these organizations what it is expected and they stay on message and the direction set by management. Review the outcomes with all the participants and management. Hold participants accountable and grade and reward them on their participation and performance.

The public is the third "We." Who exactly is the public? It's the people who live and work along the ROW. But in a broader sense, it is all the people who could be impacted by the construction, operation maintenance or failure of the pipeline. It is also the people that show a public commitment to their community and the environment. The public is also the government, whose role is clearly defined as representing the public's interest. Unfortunately, this relationship has for too long been constrained by an adversarial undercurrent. The government is scrutinized by well-intentioned advocacy groups. The government puts pressure on the regulators because of public attention, and the regulators are inclined, or required by law, to promulgate new regulations without sufficient evidence and science. Wouldn't you prefer to know and understand the values and fears of your external stakeholders before an emergency occurs? I know that the wrong time to first meet the PHMSA inspector or PHMSA regional director is at the site of an incident

We (the operators) are the public as well. We live in the communities we work in and serve. In many cases "we" live along the ROW. I know I do. If I walk a block, I can see several pipeline markers.

We need to get better at inter-generational communication as well. Times have changed, "Not only has there never been a workforce and workplace so diverse in race, gender, and ethnicity, but we also have four or five generations working side–by–side in the workplace for the first time in history. All have unique experiences and attributes that influence their attitudes towards work."[*] I have learned to communicate and transfer knowledge with a much different perspective than I had 10 years ago. "As important as it is to look at employees individually, it can be helpful to look at them through a generational lens for some predictability when trying to communicate, teach, or persuade a diverse cross-section of generations." The paper that my wife Jane and I wrote a few years ago provided me with some valuable insights and ways to improve my communications across generations. As a manager I had already implemented some of these:

---

[*] Generational Differences – J. Rau and J. Rau PPIM 2016

- Foster intergenerational teaming and learning.
- Conduct training for all leaders about generations: communication styles, preferred managerial style, how to recruit and retain. Create strategies and commit to them. Do the same for employees.
- Practice *"The Titanium Rule: Do unto others, keeping their preferences in mind."* We all try to practice the Golden Rule, but that, unfortunately, works best with people who are like us – who share similar backgrounds and preferences. With the multigenerational and diverse cultural workplace of today, the Titanium Rule is a useful skill all employees should use to show respect.
- Host meetings to discuss the strengths, needs, and interests of each employee. Open communication and appropriating each generation's strengths will not only be for the betterment of the company, but also for individual employees.
- Foster a collaborative culture where employees are encouraged to contribute new ideas, and decisions are made consensually. Create a team of employees from all departments of a company who will develop strategies for improved collaboration. This will give employees ownership of the process and product.
- Make a paradigm shift in how "training" is performed within your company. It's really about teaching and learning.
- Focus on establishing a culture of positive relationships and employees feeling valued. Consistent communication, transparency, honesty, and respect go a long way with people of all generations.
- Company leaders need to be intentional and engaged with their employees. There are many demands on leaders with today's "leaner" workforce, but the time spent with your employees in meaningful dialogue and valuing their contributions will reap the benefit of increased engagement, productivity and retention. Rather than acting as a supervisor, adapt more of a "coaching" style to help your employees learn and grow. Develop and

implement a Professional Development plan that is relevant to the individual.

People of all generations will want to work for someone who genuinely cares about them as an individual and about their growth in the company. Now is the time to verify that all generations are effectively communicating.

Why don't we know what we don't know?

Through the course of many jobs and job titles I've been asked many times, "What keeps you up at night?" Of course, as I've gotten older there are lots of things that keep me up at night. But when restricted to the real question, it is that I didn't know what I didn't know. Mostly it was, "Are we making the correct decisions in a timely fashion? Is there something else we should be doing?" I never specifically worried about a particular segment of the system, but more about what don't I know that will be problematic in the future. What could happen that we were not prepared for? Were we spending the right resources in the right places at the right time? Part of that uneasiness was borne of the knowledge that, as an Industry, we didn't (don't) spend enough on research. We need an understanding of the science of the mechanisms at play, how they initiate and grow, how to prevent them and, if they exist, how to find and characterize the resulting defects.

We don't know what we don't know because we are only reactive. Or, could it be that we're complacent and not looking? We strive to become more proactive, which should lead us to better understand what we do know. But we must move to become predictive, which forces us to look for and comprehend what we don't know. It goes back to the discussion on the journey from science to standards to regulation. We are reactive in most cases after a failure because, obviously, there was some breakdown in the process. We find out the failure cause and fix what we perceive as being broken. Hopefully we then share those lessons learned throughout the organization.

Are we truly proactive? We have lots of committees and meeting and standards. But what about the science? The numbers are not encouraging. According to the *Oil and Gas Journal*[*], natural gas pipeline revenues were $23B and hazardous liquid pipelines $25B in 2017.A typical pipeline operating company spends maybe $0.5 M a year on R&D. That's way less than 1% of revenue. PHMSA spent $121M on R&D from 2002 thru 2016. 2016 spending was $10.2M and about $4M was budgeted in 2018. The DOE 2018 R&D budget designated $387B for "Fossil Energy." I'm not sure what that includes, but probably little or none for pipelines.

We certainly need to better leverage the funds that are available, while developing a better model to increase influence and direction. PRCI has earmarked about $9M a year for pipeline research of which about 70% is directly related to pipeline threats and threat management. We certainly can and need to do more. A volunteer model with no accountability is not working. Roadmaps are not clear and distinct and not routinely shared. There is still no clear path on technology transfer.

We've mostly had a forward-looking view in this chapter. Let's not forget about the past. Our institutional knowledge is huge. With the cresting of the "silver tsunami" we may have forgotten what we do know or at least how to apply the solutions. We have come to understand a great many problems facing us and, in many cases, applied the practical solutions for them. In my recent experience I've seen the impact of incidents occurring at least in part because the knowledge of a program or process developed to address the specific cause of the incident was no longer being practiced. Each company needs to perform the research and confirm we haven't shelved these solutions, or at least determine how they could be applied more broadly

It's a journey - Reactive to Proactive to Predictive. There is a need to get ahead of the curve of understanding the things we know and uncovering what we don't know. That journey to becoming more pre-

---

[*] *Oil and Gas Journal* 10/1/2018 C. E. Smith

dictive, or in many cases starting the process, is a combination of the above two issues, not enough effort on science and not being aware of our past successes. Use what we do know and fully investigate the gaps in that knowledge. We need a clear and concise roadmap of where we are and where we need to go. It should outline the gaps and define the resources and timeline to fill those gaps. The current R&D model is not working. We need more money, a long-term commitment and, most important, accountability to confirm we stay the course.

As for the millennials, they need to get involved, stay involved, bring new ideas and the energetic attitude they are famous for. That "don't tell me I can't do that" attitude!

Are we better or worse than we think we are?

This is a summary of the issues I have discussed in this chapter and it provides some high-level observations and some points worthy of re-stating.

- ✓ Just because you can doesn't mean you should
- ✓ Collaboration is necessary but not sufficient
- ✓ The next generation has a chance to get it right

I know we're bad about communicating. I know we're bad about sharing lessons learned. I know we're bad about sharing the details of our experiences. I know we're bad about showing transparency. I know we're bad about taking advantage of our organizations' cultures. I understand some of these are difficult to change due to the competitive nature of the business. We have lawyers always there ready to help us!!

What we do have right? We have highly trained, qualified and competent people in the Industry. We have new generations in the workforce ready and able to take over for the boomers.

We need to use our current and future knowledge better; to be more productive in every aspect of pipeline operations. Use that knowledge to formulate new Industry standards. Apply the science and technology. Actively engage in R&D, find out what you don't know and become more predictive. Let the Industry standards drive the need for new regulations due to changes in technology or process solutions. It is time to look at expanding the commitment to R&D. There are insufficient resources applied (money) and no clear overall roadmap of what is needed and how to get there.

We need to continue to participate in workshops, conferences and trade associations. For the best possible outcome, the people who represent an Operator for any of these organizations need to communicate, verify with management what the company message and direction is, and verify not only commitment to the organization, but consistency in the message. Hold participants accountable and grade them on their participation and performance.

For the best possible implementation of a PSMS, get all the pieces working effectively together. We need to manage the outcomes with more detailed metrics and share the results with all parts of the organization. We must learn the lessons and share the results. Don't assume it's all in place. Survey the organization from side to side and top to bottom.

When you put it all together, I'm more optimistic than pessimistic. We certainly made great strides during my career, but even greater strides are needed. We can get there. Later chapters in this book will provide a much better insight into how others think of where we are and where we need to go.

A little bit of philosophy from a doctor of it

Dr Dave Johnson PE

> *I'd have us considering the decisions we're about to make and the actions we're about to take through the lens of our own eyes when we're 75 years old and looking into the eyes of our grandchildren, whether we have any right now or not.*

How in the world did I get here?

The short answer is, "It beats me." Purdue University was just 60 miles up the road, and all the math and science was interesting, so that was a natural. The metallurgists got to do failure investigations and tell the other engineering disciplines what they did wrong and why their stuff broke, so that was a natural, too. About the time I was finishing my B.S., the job market really sucked, so grad school – another natural. After graduation, six years in the nuclear breeder reactor power program convinced me that my future lay elsewhere. And maybe Three Mile Island was the exclamation point on that decision. (I didn't do it, by the way.) The pipeline industry beckoned, although at the time I was only vaguely aware of it, and, 40-plus years later, here we are. A composite photo would have some pipe metallurgy, failure investigations, welding, construction troubleshooting, corrosion control, new project engineering, pipeline safety and compliance, integrity management, agency interactions and responses, standards development, trade associations, lobbying, and research and development. The transformation from newbie in the business to the old guy who has been there forever happens in a heartbeat.

> *"I'd love to change the world, but I don't know what to do.*
> *So I'll leave it up to you."*
> —Alvin Lee (1971)

Some time ago, Jerry, who frequently said, *"By God, if I were in charge, we'd ..."* noted that would be a great book, because there were probably a bunch of people who had similar thoughts. And he was going to put it together. With some poking and prodding, he got a number of us to say sure, we would contribute some thoughts to this project. Kudos to Jerry for following through and herding the cats to get this done.

When he approached me, he said something like: *"You've been around forever, like since the days of wooden pipelines and corrosion control using DDT, before it was banned, to keep the termites from eating the wood. Surely, you can come up with something for this."* But when I looked at the other authors, I was thinking I know a bit about all of the subjects suggested, but not as much as the person writing about it. I'm not going to try to talk about a subject covered much more knowledgeably by someone else in the same volume.

I find it a bit interesting, if only to me, that I am writing this almost 50 years to the day after the Woodstock festival – three days of peace and love. No, I not going to claim I was there. I was not. But the enduring feeling was one of both idealism, a desire to make the world better, and restlessness. So where are we today, why do we do what we do, and what do we want to leave behind? Does that idealism and restlessness survive, and how do we nurture it?

We get out of school and start our careers, young, eager, idealistic, ready to change the world and perhaps have a bit of fun and excitement along the way, although some may argue that many engineers have non-traditional definitions of fun and excitement. We want to do good stuff and make a difference. And we should.

But for many of us, reality creeps in, and the demands of everyday living sort of get in the way of that vision. There are house payments, car payments, getting the air conditioner fixed, all those clothes for the kids, who seem to outgrow them in a matter of days, saving for or paying off college, an occasional, much-needed vacation, and all of the mid-career pressures to succeed and to follow company policies and be part of the company culture. So, by the time the kids are off on their own, and it's time for you, your elderly parents need a bit more of your attention. And after that, you are the elderly parents. Holy cow, what happened? How did it happen so fast? What happened to my plans? Did I make a difference? Can I still? The answer is yes.

> *"Hold on tight to your dream."*
> —Jeff Lynne (1981)

If you are reading this book, chances are you have some connection to the energy pipeline industry. Those of us who have spent some time in this industry, over 40 years for me now, ought to be asking ourselves what should we be doing, how should we be doing it, and why. Always why. Why do we need to do better – don't we always hear that pipelines are the safest form of energy transportation, at least for hydrocarbons? Here's a start on why we have to be better. In my lifetime, the population of the United States has increased by a factor of about 2.3. Pipeline mileage has approximately tripled. And total energy consumption has about tripled, with oil and natural gas consumption more than quadrupling. We have more and more people living in closer proximity to more and more pipelines, which transport critical energy at increasingly higher pressures and throughputs (inherently hazardous commodities). If we fail to do our jobs to make sure these pipelines operate safely, there is an increasing potential for bad outcomes. Who are all these people living and working and playing and traveling in proximity to the pipelines? Well, some of them are my children and my grandchildren and my nieces and nephews and their children and in-laws. Some are yours. All of them are someone's family, loved ones, friends. They all deserve our best.

What is our best, and how do we know if we're doing it? It is easy to rationalize decisions. There are budgetary pressures to spend less. There are the justifications that the regulations don't really require it. "It's probably ok." "I'm sure it is good enough." But is it? A colleague once told me, "If you keep lowering your aim, you end up shooting yourself in the foot." How do we recognize if we are lowering our aim too much? One way is to examine the expectations that society has of us and do a self-assessment as to whether we are meeting them. A relatively straightforward and concise expression of those expectations is embodied in the Code of Ethics for Engineers. While we may not all be degreed engineers or registered professional engineers, this is still good guidance. Some of these canons and obligations include:

- Hold paramount the safety, health and welfare of the public.
- Perform services only in the area of competence.
- Avoid deceptive acts.
- Conduct oneself honorably, responsibly, ethically and lawfully.
- Avoid conflicts of interest.

I find it interesting to note that in the fourth item above, "lawfully" is last in the list and is preceded by "honorably, responsibly, ethically." Our conduct should, of course, be lawful. However, lawful is a necessary, but not sufficient, condition. We also have to hit the first three. There is no "or" between these. These are all bits of advice and guidance that we are certainly aware of. But it helps to occasionally look at them in written form and ask, "Am I doing these things?"

> *"Teach your children well. And feed them on your dreams.*
> *The one they pick's the one you'll know by."*
> —Graham Nash (1969)

In mid-career, there are not only the job pressures, but also all of the family pressures, activities and demands. These pressures are physical, financial, psychological, emotional, you name it. Thinking about a legacy just isn't on the radar screen. But as one nears the end of a career, it is. What have I taught my coworkers, my children, my grandchildren? Go along to get along, or do what's right? Oh, it's good enough, or we can do better? Someone else will take care of it, or clean up our own messes? I think some of the other contributors here will agree – grandchildren give you a different perspective on the world. Whatever we do, whatever kind of world we create or leave, they will have to deal with it, without us. It is a huge responsibility. It is, therefore, a responsibility that one needs to keep in mind every day.

Speaking of grandchildren, whether you are reading this early, mid or later in your life and career, you are probably working with people who are not too different in age from your grandparents, parents, children or even grandchildren. What are you learning from them, and what are they learning from you? Take the time to ask your questions and to pass along some of life's lessons, especially those you wish you had learned earlier.

> *"Will you still need me; will you still feed me, when I'm sixty-four?"*
> —John Lennon and Paul McCartney (1966)

I actually had this posted on my door for a while the year I turned sixty-four. It is a question that we ask ourselves throughout our lives and careers, but it becomes a bit more pointed as age advances. Am I doing anything beneficial? Do I have a purpose? Everyone wants to feel useful. So, make yourself useful. If you are younger, seek out the geezer down the hall. He may not be as grumpy as he appears and may have some knowledge or experience that is useful to you. If you are one of the geezers, keep your door open, figuratively and literally. You are not valuable because you know things; you are valuable because you share that knowledge. There have been generational studies that show the baby boomers (rapidly becoming geezers) and the millennials in the workplace usually get along exceptionally well. It is attributed to the millennials being unafraid to ask questions and the boomers feeling useful because the millennials seek them out. Do not hesitate to ask; and do not hesitate to share when asked.

> *"I wish that I knew what I know now when I was younger."*
> —Ronnie Lane and Ron Wood (1973)

It is not too late. Tomorrow, anything you learn today, will be something you learned when you were younger. Not by much, maybe, but every little bit helps. Whether Jerry had this explicitly or implicitly in mind when he sought input for this collection, here it is. It is difficult to imagine grandchildren, or great-grandchildren, let alone think about what they will be facing, when your own kids are toddlers and starting school. So the contributors here have tried to do that. There are some good lessons here, and I think all of them bear on the subject of ethics, legacy and personal responsibility. Trust me, you really do not want to ever be the person thinking "I knew that was going to happen. Maybe if I had spoken up, it could have been prevented." I think you will be pleasantly surprised at the support you get. And you will certainly sleep better at night. We are the people responsible for our pipelines. It is an awesome responsibility. However, if we remain inquisitive and committed, the industry will get better and everyone will benefit.

Probably few of us technical types actually undertake much study of philosophy per se. There are several definitions of philosophy. Those generally gravitate toward "the study of general and fundamental problems concerning matters such as existence, knowledge, values, reason, mind and language," "the study of the fundamental nature of knowledge, reality, and existence," and "a theory or attitude held by a person or organization that acts as a guiding principle for behavior." When we think of philosophers, we maybe think of people like Plato, Aristotle, Socrates, Thomas Aquinas, René Descartes, John Locke, Voltaire, Alexis de Tocqueville, John Stuart Mill, Susan B. Anthony and many others. However, as I have tried to point out, there are little tidbits everywhere, if you take a few moments to reflect about the messages offered and what they might mean to you. This volume represents knowledge acquired through literally hundreds of years of work, study and experience. If you are a pipeliner, there is undoubtedly something in here that you did not know but can make good use of. That is our task and our responsibility. Make it better. And don't get discouraged. Just remember,

> *"You can't always get what you want. But if you try sometimes,*
> *you just might find, you get what you need."*
> —Keith Richards and Mick Jagger (1969)

One person's perspective on cultivating technical leadership in the pipeline industry

William A. Bruce, P.E., IWE, CWEng*

> *BY GOD, IF I WERE IN CHARGE...*

> *I'd advise the Industry how to educate, train, mentor, and prepare the next generation of pipeline engineers for technical leadership. The Industry will fail without a constant supply of new competent technical leaders.*

How did I get here?

After a miserable experience in high school (I was a classic un-der-achiever), I finally hit my stride at the Ohio State University, where I earned a bachelor's degree in Welding Engineering. My first real job was in the Technical Services Division at Panhandle Eastern Pipeline Company in Kansas City, Missouri, where I spent eight years. I then joined Edison Welding Institute in Columbus, Ohio, where I was involved in pipeline welding research and development for the next 18 years. For the past 13 years, I have been at DNV GL in Columbus where

---

* With a little help from my friends.

I focus mainly on helping pipeline operating companies implement "industry best practices."

Introduction

The pipeline industry needs a constant supply of new competent technical leaders. Others are better suited to discuss the "silver tsunami" in our industry and what do in its aftermath, but how do you become a technical leader and why would you want to? There is the obvious potential benefit of increasing your earning potential as you move up the ladder, but I would suggest that you do it not just because it's beneficial for you, but that you should do it for the betterment of society. The world in general, and our Industry in particular, needs leaders in technical fields. Young people of the current generation can have a positive impact on future generations by aspiring to be technical leaders today. Admit it – you didn't get into the field of engineering to get rich anyway, did you? It must have been for the impact you thought you could make on future generations.

I've been around the block a few times and I suppose that somebody, somewhere, considers me to be a leader in my narrow field of expertise. However, I hadn't thought much about how I got to where I am until I was invited to participate on a panel session on cultivating technical leadership in the pipeline industry. Some of the practices that I offered during that panel session and that follow in this chapter I am not very good at myself. If I do appear to be good at them, it's because I have to work very hard at it. Writing this chapter is hard for me because the act of doing so is actually contrary to some of what follows in this chapter.

The earlier you start down the path to technical leadership the more impact you can make during your career. Figure 1 is a graph of some measure of technical leadership – it could be prominence, name recognition, esteem, etc., but let's call it prominence – as a function of time. It's a lot like saving for retirement – the earlier you start, the more significant the impact of your efforts will be. The same goes for the harder you work at it, which is shown for a given starting point in Figure 2.

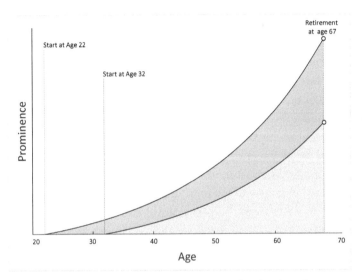

Figure 1. Graph of prominence versus age showing effect of starting early.

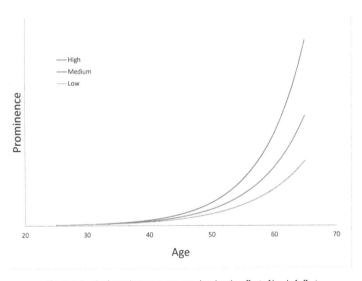

Figure 2. Graph of prominence versus age showing the effect of level of effort.

Be a good communicator

We all learned early on about the importance of communicating well – both orally and in the writing. Both take practice. You may feel uncomfortable speaking in public or speaking to those in positions of authority, but I guarantee that it is natural to feel that way. I still get nervous before a presentation and I suspect that everyone does to some extent. Learn how to take constructive criticism in your communication skills and apply what you learn.

Be good at technical writing. Think back to the technical reports and journal articles you have read. Which ones were easiest to understand and made the most memorable impression? Which ones forced you to re-read passages to try to understand what the author was saying? Learn to write from the best examples and learn from the errors of others. Have something to share, and be willing and able to share! Take the time to write a journal article. Even if it is not accepted for publication, the act of preparing the article forces you to crystallize your thoughts and critically assess the defensibility of your opinions and recommendations.* Alternately, you can always share it with colleagues via Internet forums, or just file it away for further refinement in the future.

Be proactive in your communications. Keep your clients informed, whether they are internal staff in your own organization or external clients. If you ever get asked "Will you still be able to provide the deliverable today?" you have failed in your communication efforts. A quick, one-line email message confirming that everything is on schedule as planned prevents making your clients guess how things are going.

Don't just forward FYI emails. That's not communication. Explain why and how the information contained is useful or outline the tasks that need to be accomplished. Merely sending an email does not transfer the responsibility to the receiver.

---

* The first article I submitted for publication was an assignment from my technical writing course while I was still at Ohio State. While it wasn't a true technical journal (*Motocross Action* magazine), it was accepted and I got paid $50 for it!

Remember that almost no one likes meetings. They can be interruptions to otherwise potentially productive time. Don't have meetings to disseminate information. Instead, reserve meetings for situations when active discussion or brainstorming is required.

Don't get consumed by social media and electronic communications. Call or visit someone instead of instant messaging, texting, or sending an email. There is less likelihood of being misunderstood or misinterpreted if you say it in person or on the phone. This is something I have to work hard at.

In speaking with people who have a different background than you (e.g., engineers speaking with tradespeople), do your best to speak "their language." Tradespeople are not going to be impressed by the breadth of your technical vocabulary.

Be a good person

In his book, *All I Really Need to Know I Learned in Kindergarten,* Robert Fulghum suggests that the lessons we learned during this time in our lives should be used as a foundation for the rest of our lives. If you make a mess, clean it up. Share! Being a diligent follower of some of these things you learned in kindergarten will make you feel better about yourself and will make you more likeable.

Don't forget the Golden Rule: *Do unto others as you would have them do unto you.* Someone recently introduced me to the Titanium Rule; *Do onto others with their druthers in minds.* The idea is to put yourself in their shoes and consider the outcome they would like to see. You might not always decide that outcome is best, but at least you will have considered multiple viewpoints. In the end, be prepared to defend your decision. "Because I said so" is not a useful response to adults.

Share

Don't keep work just because the lead came to you. Pass it along to whomever is best suited to do it, even if they are outside your organization. It will come back to you in droves. In other words, the confidence and altruism you show by passing something along will be rewarded. Ask to be kept in the loop so that you can learn from how the other expert addresses the issue. There is value in learning a bit about other technical topics that are outside your own area of expertise. Staying in the loop also helps ensure that the person you handed the lead off to is responding in a timely fashion ("trust but verify"). How well your colleague completes the work can be a reflection on you, for good or bad.

Be humble

Most people don't like working with a know-it-all. Worse yet is having to work with someone who proclaims to know it all, but doesn't. Even though you may have complete knowledge of a given situation or technical problem, don't over-publicize that from the beginning. I've found that the best way to get someone to accept an idea or way of thinking is to make them think it was their idea! In other words, listen to their problem and reflect it back in the form of a solution using their words.

This thought of humility is one of the things that made this chapter difficult for me to write– the mere act of telling someone to be humble is not humble! By writing this chapter, I'm proclaiming to be an expert at how to become a technical leader, which is not a humble thing to do.

Have integrity

Don't cheat. Do what's right. For consultants, the financial interest of the company may sometimes be at odds with what is right. If you don't believe me, go see the movie *Jerry Maguire.*[*]

---

[*] Jerry understood the soft side of the business. The company was only interested in financial performance at all cost. The company didn't appreciate Jerry's mission statement, which involved better service to a fewer number of clients. SPOILER ALERT: Jerry got fired but ended up happy.

Don't be tempted to defend someone else's bad actions or bad technical decisions just because they are willing to pay you for it. The short-term gain is not worth compromising your integrity.

Be dependable. Stick to your commitments. Unforeseen circumstances might make that impossible, and when they do, re-read the section above regarding communication. Clients, whether internal or external, might be disappointed in the news, but not as disappointed as they will be when the agreed deadline comes and goes with no deliverable and no prior notification.

Be lucky

While it sounds a bit off the wall, you can indeed make your own luck. I learned a long time ago that luck happens when preparedness meets opportunity. Being prepared is what you have as a result of your education and experience. Doing some of the things I've outlined in this chapter, like being a good person, will tend to make people like you, which can open a lot of doors. In other words, doing whatever you can to make people like you creates the potential for lots of opportunities. I'll say it again - luck happens when preparedness meets opportunity.

Don't make mistakes

Telling someone not to make mistakes may sound obvious, but knowing the components that determine risk factors might keep you from doing something stupid. Risk is probability multiplied by consequence (Figure 3). If something is unlikely to happen and, even if it does, the consequences will be relatively harmless, the risk is insignificant. It's the other corner of the risk matrix in Figure 3 where significant attention should be focused.

When you do make mistakes, which inevitably happens, learn from them.

3 x 3 Risk Matrix

Likely	**Medium Risk**	**High Risk**	**Extreme Risk**
Unlikely	**Low Risk**	**Medium Risk**	**High Risk**
Highly Unlikely	**Insignificant Risk**	**Low Risk**	**Medium Risk**
	Slightly Harmful	**Harmful**	**Extremely Harmful**

L
I
K
E
L
I
H
O
O
D

CONSEQUENCES

Figure 3. Risk Matrix figure.

Manage expectations

In the promises you make (e.g., project deliverables), be sure to spell out the uncertainties. Sometimes being the technical expert means not providing "the" answer, but providing a range of possible answers. Remember, there can be more than one way to make an acceptable weld, repair a pipeline, prevent corrosion, or design a tank, just as there is more than one way to do lots of things. Provide options, not just a single path forward, and describe the advantages and limitations of each option. Sometimes the client is in the best position to select the best among various options. Your job is to give them the tools to make the best decision for their unique circumstances.

Find a good life partner

Life is a journey that is best experienced with a partner. I'm not sure why I felt compelled to include this thought in this chapter, but having a good life partner has certainly been an important part of who I have become both personally and professionally.

Stimulate the other side of your brain

We are engineers, so we tend to have plenty of stimulation for the left side of our brain. No one wants an unbalanced brain, so explore the beauty of art, music, theater, etc. Take a walk in the park, embrace geography, travel. Read a book without any technical content! Stimulate your brain in general by doing crossword puzzles.

Pass it on

One measure of success is not how much you know, but how much you pass on. In other words, success can be measured by the extent to which you helped others become competent so they can build upon your technical successes. When you are gone, be missed for the loss of your inspiration, not just for the loss of your expertise (although you should pass that along, too).

Be a mentor. Hire interns. Help junior staff identify technical interests and give them the opportunity to explore those interests. Facilitating enthusiasm is a big part of promoting technical development. Don't overlook opportunities to expose others to something new. It is easy to forget that junior staff and interns often don't know what they will like or dislike because they don't even know some of the technical challenges that exist. Likewise, help them identify what they need to improve in, and help them build a roadmap toward improvement. It doesn't have to always be done as part of a formal annual review and goal-setting process.

Things like technical conferences inspire me. I always come away with a list of great ideas. Attend a technical conference and even consider joining the leadership team. Be involved in the process. Set the example for our successors to follow. If you are a leader on a committee or symposium, document what you do and how you do it. Pass it on so those who follow don't have to reinvent the wheel. They might choose to do something differently, but nothing is more difficult than starting with a blank sheet of paper. Let them edit and add to what you started.

Summary and conclusions

Leaders are well rounded people who are good at many things not just their technical expertise. Leaders are humble and good people who never stop listening and learning. They are multidimensional mentors involved in the process, the means, and the people, not just the outcomes.

Transfer of knowledge: training versus teaching and learning (I train my dog)

Jane Rau, CLO Jtrain Inc

> *I would help the Pipeline Industry to see that current practices in transferring knowledge could be vastly improved by tapping into the "Education Industry." It would be a paradigm shift indeed.*

How I got to where I am

I want to set the record straight from the get-go: I am a teacher, not an engineer or a technical person. I happen to be married to the guy who organized this book and who has been an engineer in the pipeline industry for 44+ years. I've learned quite a bit about the industry through "osmosis." I have also been an educator for 40+ years, from a classroom teacher to a consultant working with failing school districts all over the United States. This chapter is about how transfer of knowledge currently is practiced in the Industry and how it could be improved.

Let's also set the record straight about the word "training." I train my dog, not people. I teach people and facilitate their learning. Henceforth the word "training" will be replaced with "teaching" or a "learning opportunity." The word "trainer" will be replaced with "teacher" or "instructor."

Please allow me to claim some "street cred." I haven't just learned about the Pipeline Industry through my husband. For the past three years I've been working on a Pipeline Research Council International (PRCI) project researching how transfer of knowledge occurs in teaching non-destructive examination (NDE) technicians. (prci.org) I have observed many classes presented by many global service providers. I have also interviewed many owner/operators and service providers regarding their "education programs." Through this research I have learned a great deal about "education" in the Industry.

A question you may be asking yourself right now

Why is a teacher contributing to this book?

Good question! The Oil and Gas Industry has tapped into the aviation, nuclear and military industries as far as writing standards and procedures are concerned. But they have never tapped into the "Education Industry" for help with standards, procedures, and transfer of knowledge (learning). Being a knowledgeable Subject Matter Expert (SME) does not guarantee an ability to teach or an understanding of how learning is best achieved.

Leaning can be... wait for it... FUN! And interactive and engaging, and it can foster curiosity to learn more! It makes no difference if you are an NDE instructor, a high school algebra teacher, or a company department head. There are research-based learning strategies in education to help you improve knowledge transfer. You can use these anyplace you are attempting to transfer knowledge to help someone actually **learn** what you want them to know and not rotely memorize to spit back on a test and then forget it (I call that cognitive bulimia).

Learning objectives

A good teacher always begins with the end in mind: What is it that I want you to know (knowledge) and be able to do (transfer) after reading this chapter? In other words, what is "the big picture?" I want you to know current practices in education, some researched-based learning strategies, and begin a paradigm shift on how the Industry can improve transfer of knowledge, starting with yourself!

Why is this relevant?

Every day we transfer knowledge: to our children, spouses, friends, and colleagues. Think of all the information you "teach" people on a daily basis. Sometimes it may just seem like a conversation, but usually some kind of knowledge is being conveyed. But, when knowledge transfer involves the safety of people we care about (think of teaching a child how to cross the street safely, riding a bike, and eventually driving a car), and employees of and the public affected by the pipeline industry (for example, teaching an NDE technician to be competent), we want to be sure that the knowledge has truly been transferred and learned. As I stated earlier, in education there are research-based learning strategies that can be used to promote true learning, not just rote memorization to pass a test. But before I discuss these, let's begin to build the foundation for this learning opportunity.

The Adult Learner

Pedagogy is the art and science of how children learn. It is teacher directed. Andragogy is the art and science of how adults learn. It is student directed and teacher facilitated. In the 1960's and early 1970's, Malcolm Knowles* built a comprehensive theory of adult learning that

---

* Knowles, M. (1990) The adult learner. A neglected species, 4th Edition. Houston: Gulf Publishing.

is anchored in the characteristics of adult learners. He resurrected the term "Andragogy" that was originally coined by a German educator in 1833. (In Latin, Andragogy literally means "leader of man") The characteristics of adult learners are:

The need to know - Adults need to know why they need to learn something before undertaking to learn it.

The learner's self-concept - Adults have a self-concept of being responsible for their own decisions, for their own lives. Once they have arrived at that self-concept they develop a deep psychological need to be seen by others and treated by others as being capable of self-direction.

The role of the learner's experience - Adults come into educational activity with both a greater volume and a different quality of experience from youths.

Readiness to learn - Adults become ready to learn those things they need to know and be able to do in order to cope effectively with their real-life situation.

Orientation to learning - In contrast to children's and youths' subject-centered orientation to learning (at least in school), adults are life-centered (or task-centered or problem-centered) in their orientation to learning.

Motivation - While adults are responsive to some external motivators (better jobs, promotions, higher salaries, and the like), the most potent motivators are internal pressures (the desire for increased job satisfaction, self-esteem, quality of life and the like). (Knowles 1990, p.57-63)

Much of what I observed during the course of my research project for PRCI is that most NDE instructors, SMEs and Level IIIs are highly knowledgeable, but they teach the same way they were taught in school. Their students were mostly in rows or at a table, and the instructor would read from or refer to a PowerPoint didactically instructing. This appears to be pervasive in the industry. This is in direct conflict with how adults best learn. But one can't expect instructors or anyone trying to transfer knowledge to know what they don't know...

Improve instructor effectiveness

Have you ever taken a class or course that you passed or even did well on the exam, but you had no idea what the class was all about? I've asked that question to well over 1,000 adults with zero "no" responses. We "jumped through the hoops" to do whatever we needed to do to pass the course. No real learning occurred. If you can only recall and state something, you don't really understand it. You have to be able to explain and justify its meaning, and you also have to be able to apply it into settings where it is needed without being prompted to do so. That is true knowledge transfer.

So, how can the Pipeline Industry improve how knowledge is transferred? Has anyone who teaches classes or courses or transfers knowledge taken a "Train the Trainer" course that is actually vetted and focused to include research-based learning strategies? In my research, I found very few of these courses. Two allowed me to observe, and they had some great ideas, but none of their curriculum was written by anyone with a background in education. Over the duration of the course, no learning strategies were implemented to verify student learning or modeled (demonstrated) so the students could then implement them when they taught their own classes. This reality leads me to strongly recommend that both the name and focus of these courses be changed to Instructor Effectiveness. But, here's the Catch-22 (and I hope you Millennials and Gen Z-ers get the reference): how can one take an Instructor Effectiveness course that includes research-based learning strategies if that doesn't exist – yet? Take it upon yourself to do some research on how you can help make these courses happen. Talk to your management. Find educators who are well versed in research-based learning strategies to help reimagine existing "Train the Trainer" courses. While you're at it, Google some of the following learning strategies:

- Essential question
- Aligned and relevant learning objectives
- Formative assessment
- Self-assessment

- Rubrics for assessment/self-assessment
- Use of video to improve teacher effectiveness (video instructor teaching a class)
- Student seating for collaboration
- Learning style survey
- Questioning – wait time
- Levels of questions
- Random selection
- Immediate and specific feedback
- Writing aligned and effective multiple-choice questions
- Making connections to schema to generate learning and transfer
- Use of instructor/mentors who have successfully used learning strategies; coaching
- Backward design
- Flipped classroom
- Scaffolding
- Task analysis
- Mutual expectations/setting norms

Please understand that in order to implement many of these strategies with fidelity, one must learn the strategy first, and then see it modeled (demonstrated) in a classroom or meeting setting. I have worked with teachers all over the United States, and that is what I found to be true – even with other educators!

Case in point – formative assessment. John Hattie, a world-renowned educational researcher performed a meta-analysis of research on learning strategies and found that formative assessment is one of the most effective strategies a teacher can implement to improve student learning. Formative assessment is a range of formal and informal assessment procedures conducted by teachers during the learning process in order to modify teaching and learning activities to improve student learning. **Form**ative assessment is used during the **form**ing of learning; **sum**mative assessment tests the **sum**mation of learning – the final exam. Formative assessment drives the instruction. Where are your students in their learning? Do I need to back up and reteach because they don't quite "get it" yet? You are checking for your students' understanding.

There are many ways to formatively assess your students'/participants' learning progress (Google formative assessment). But, if you walk away with anything after reading this chapter, I hope you walk away with this: if you are transferring knowledge in a meeting or teaching a class, do not ask, "Are there any questions?" Or, my favorite, "Does that make sense?" Generally, the people who ask questions are those who really don't need to – they already "get it," and the people who should be asking questions do not because they don't want to appear stupid. That is particularly true of the adult learner. So, to engage all learners along this continuum I recommend you use a formative assessment technique called "Fist to 5." I won't be able to model this for you, but I will explain it to the best of my ability. Fist to 5 is akin to a Likert Scale – much like when you are sent a survey and they want to know on a scale of 0 to 5 what your opinion is. In Fist to 5, the hand is the "scale."

Fist (0) = never or I totally don't understand
1 finger = rarely or hardly at all
2 fingers = occasionally
3 fingers = sometimes
4 fingers = frequently
5 fingers = consistently – I could teach this to anyone

Before you use this technique, you need to teach your students/participants how to perform this correctly if they have never done it before. If you skip this step, the technique will not work. Trust me. Start with something they already know about, like Halloween. Explain what the fist through 5 fingers equal as shown above. Then make the following statement: "To what extent is Halloween your favorite holiday?" Tell them they may not show you their answer until you say something like "show me" or "okay." Wait three to five seconds – and you should do this whenever you ask a question of anyone because we all process auditory information at different speeds. We are not all auditory learners. Some of us are visual or kinesthetic learners. Then, when you give them the signal to respond, they should all show their response at the same time. You may have to practice this a few times. If they don't all show together, they may look around to see what the other responses are and simply copy them. Yes, even adults do this – they are usually worse than the kids!

Once they know how to perform Fist to 5, you can then use the technique when transferring knowledge. After presenting some instruction (preferably no more than five minutes), stop and say, "To what extent do you understand _____?" (Fill in what information or concept you were trying to help them learn.) Examples: "To what extent do you understand this safety procedure?" "To what extent do you understand this part of the PHMSA standard?" "To what extent do you understand how this will apply to your department?" If you see many fists, 1s and 2s, you need to go back and reteach. If you see mostly 3s, 4s, and 5s, you can continue, but keep an eye on the 3s.

The beautiful thing about this type of formative assessment is that the students are self-assessing. They are thinking about their thinking, which makes them metacognitive. They are engaged in their learning. You are formatively assessing them to see where they are in their learning which will drive your instruction. (Note: if everyone is always showing 5s, have them give you evidence of their learning. 5s are not something you should see often.) So now you know one way to formatively assess students' understanding! (Another note: I taught this to my husband who gives many learning opportunities regarding standards and regulations in the Pipeline Industry. He uses it regularly and says it has made him a better instructor, and the adult students love the fact that they can show their level of understanding without feeling judged. Misconceptions can be addressed immediately.)

Why can't we all share?

One thing that really stood out during the course of my PRCI project research is the unwillingness of owner/operators, service providers, and professional organizations in the Industry to share with each other programs they had developed based on failures and errors. I understand IP, commercial protections and the search for the almighty dollar, but when it comes to the safety of people and protection of property, shouldn't this be shared? If the pipeline industry establishes a collective mindfulness and works **together**, sharing their errors, near misses, and what they have found to be effective in mitigating those experiences, wouldn't this make the system as potent as possible in the face of its human hazards? Implement a culture of sharing from within and outside your organization. This may not have a direct relationship to transfer of knowledge, but I feel it is an important element in a culture that seeks to optimize knowledge development, deployment, and transfer.

Can the industry move from a training culture to a learning culture?

Change the paradigm from training to learning. It starts with you...

Is the pipeline industry investable?

Shawn Laughlin, BS ChE, MBA

> *I would mandate that every pipeline industry Senior Manager take a once-per-year written examination on pipeline fundamentals, mechanical integrity, and risk management.*

The results would then be documented and published within annual financial reports, or available via the Internet. This would cause every Manager to prepare. They would know or learn the technical basics of the industry. The public and investors would see the examination results, so poor results would likely not happen often. Senior managers would be forced to consider and have the basis to evaluate the integrity of the systems within the decision framework of the enterprise. All stakeholders benefit at almost no cost.[*]

---

[*] The intent is to avoid specific prescriptive regulation of each detail and to avoid the potential for performance based regulation to obscure risks or allow unrecognized threats to lead to negative events that could be statistically inevitable with the passage of sufficient time. Further the intent is to insure that senior management has the background and tools to make the well-evaluated asset allocation decisions. The essence of pipeline integrity decision making as viewed from the point of view of senior management may well be: to insure the integrity of a pipeline system, "never spend one more dollar than needed, but for god's sakes, never spend one less penny than needed to keep the pipeline safe". This may require the Wisdom of Solomon, the intent of my decree, is to verify that senior management knows the proper areas to review to evaluate both the dollars and the pennies.

How'd I get here?

Tioga County, New York is about 200 miles northwest of New York City. I grew up in the Town of Owego, the county seat. In many regards it was a wonderful place, peaceful, no major crime, no urban decay, parades through town on major holidays. The teachers and administrators of the public schools lived in town and cared about educational results and the kids. Economic opportunities were difficult to envision, no mines, no significant factories, no obvious careers, not much employment of any kind. An engineering degree from Cornell University seemed like a credential that might help provide opportunities. I graduated in 1984, a rather significant oil and gas industry slump was happening, a job offer from Lincoln Electric, as a sales engineer in the welding industry, was obtained and accepted. I knew nothing about welding. Lincoln immediately sent us to welding school; they firmly believed that to sell welding products, you needed to know how to use them. I learned how to weld. The training program was "hands on," and lasted almost a full year. At the end of it they sent me to Connecticut. It was there that the customers really taught me about welding and the welding industry.

In 1986 I bought a 3-acre parcel of land in Owego. This property has no road frontage but had an easement along a pipeline right-of-way to access that land. The pipeline right-of-way also ran along the eastern boundary of my three acres. Buying this property was my first real introduction to pipelines and property owner topics. I still own this parcel. For over three decades I've had a front-row seat to stakeholder issues related to pipelines.

In the late 1980s, while working for Lincoln, I served as Chairman of the Connecticut Section of the American Welding Society. I also decided to pursue an MBA from the University of Connecticut, with concentrations in International Business and Finance. This was conferred in 1991. In 1994 I accepted the position of International Regional Manager for the countries of the former Soviet Union. This was a time of immense change in geopolitics. The Cold War had ended. The economies of these countries had collapsed, oil and gas and pipelines were the dominant activities. I spent about 120 days a year in Russia and the other former republics. Pipeline construction was the focus. In 1998, I was offered a position as President and CEO of a company that manufactured and marketed a fiber composite pipeline reinforcement system. I was 35 years old, the risk/reward calculations seemed rational. I accepted the position and served in that capacity for almost 19 years. It was during these years that Pipeline integrity and the related topics were a prime focus. I cannot claim that my career within the pipeline industry was planned, targeted or intentional.

Introduction

I cannot suggest what is right and what is wrong with the pipeline industry without some circumspection and contemplation on how you would evaluate the health of the industry. Facts and measures of performance obviously could be considered. Performance metrics should involve financial performance, social well-being, societal benefits, employee satisfaction, environmental impact, and specific stakeholder metrics. A fair and proper evaluation must begin with an overview.

My preferred method of inquiry is to minimize data and simply ask: Is the industry investable? That is:

- Is the industry worthy of an investment of your hard-earned retirement dollars? Will it produce economic returns? Is such an investment likely to be adequate and secure over time?
- Are you comfortable suggesting the industry as a long-term career selection for your children or grandchildren?

Answers to these questions cannot be complete and precise without some speculation regarding the future. Past performance data can be rather easily acquired, but you need to dust off the crystal ball and consider the future for a proper answer. I suggest that it helps to comprehend where one is going if one knows where one has been. The Pipeline Industry has been a vehicle for great wealth accumulation over the last 30 years. The multinational oil companies decided to a large extent that their capital was best invested in production and exploration, and that they could monetize and divest pipeline assets or businesses and use the proceeds more productively. On the other side of these transactions were entities or individuals who saw opportunity and willingly acquired pipeline assets. Regulation and government actions provided incentives in the form of preferential taxation for Master Limited Partnerships (MLP's), and the predictable cash flow of often regulated transportation services provided the mechanism for leverage and monetization. Several great fortunes were amassed. Pipeline cash flow was also utilized to fund enterprises that ultimately failed in spectacular fashion. While the business history is fascinating, our efforts need to be focused on the future and the viability of the industry. Is the pipeline industry a viable investment for your money? Is the pipeline industry a viable investment for your children's or grandchildren's careers?

I will attempt to offer answers to these questions and provide some rational for further evaluation later in this chapter. Prior to this, a few stories are offered to illustrate symptoms, concerns or challenges, and perhaps suggest some insight into the issues of future performance of the pipeline industry.

The true tale of Injun Joe
August 1991

The car phone rang. (There was a day and age when cell phones were not ubiquitous. People with wealth, or those who traveled via passenger vehicle for business purposes, were likely to have a car phone.) I traveled around the New England states as a technical sales engineer of welding equipment and consumables. I had met some modest career success, had served as chairperson of the Connecticut Section of the American Welding Society for a couple of terms, and was generally well known in the welding industry of the New England region.

The caller requested immediate attention to a welding problem. Welds on new construction of a hospital addition were cracking. Construction was on hold until the weld cracking issues were resolved. In 1991, weld cracking issues on new construction were not common.

Construction sites are typically quite easy to locate; just look for structural steel or cranes. I located the site, drove in, put on my hard hat and walked toward a group of gentlemen speaking with great animation and fervor. The hard hat had my company's logo and rapidly identified me as a person to blame. The fervor and great animation of the heated discussion was rapidly thrust upon my welding equipment, my welding electrode, and me. It was assumed I had to be to blame. It was assumed the problem was obviously the supplier of the welding equipment and welding consumables.

This was not my first rodeo. I had been employed for perhaps seven years by the welding products manufacturer, attended one full year of welding school and training following my Ivy League engineering education, and had at least six years in the field as a technical sales engineer. But cracked structural steel construction welds were a novelty.

From previous training and experience, I was rather certain that the preheat requirements for the material were not precisely the same and varied by thickness. I was suspicious of 4-inch thick flanges and dual certifications on the structural steel. I had not seen this combination before. I then used the car phone to call corporate headquarters to speak with the welding technology department. I also commented that the sheer volume of steel being used appeared to be massively in excess of traditional construction.

The knowledgeable welding technology department quickly indicated that they had seen only one similar situation and it had been a few weeks prior. While the steel met all of the requirements of both the A36 grade and the A572 grade 50 material, the AWS welding code specified a much higher preheat for the A572 grade 50 (pre-heat was utilized to slow down the cooling rate and avoid cracking). The solution was to use much greater preheat. Newly armed with this verification, it was time to return to the interested parties for a discussion.

I reported that the fix involved a change of welding procedure, with only the preheat and interpass temperatures being altered.

As I explained that preheat was required, a welder walked around the corner. He was an imposing figure who stood about 6 foot 8 inches tall. He listened for a few minutes while the steel fabricator, the steel erector, and the hospital representative all wanted assurances that the preheat would resolve the cracking issue. The welder spoke up and introduced himself as "Injun Joe." Structural steel erectors had a significant portion of their employees with ethic Native American heritage. They were considered to be excellent steel erectors, great welders, and fearless of heights. Joe was proud of his self-given moniker and made sure everyone knew it. Joe informed me that he had told everyone involved that they needed to preheat but nobody would listen because, as he offered, "I'm just a dumb welder."

Joe and I were tasked with providing proof of an effective resolution. We were to preheat a column joint and weld. The inspection of the weld would be the following morning. The true purpose of preheat of a welded joint is to slow down the cooling rate of the steel. You need to avoid a fast quench and thus eliminate a grain structure susceptible to cracks. Preheat was applied via a fuel gas torch equipped with a "rosebud" tip to spread the heat over a wide area. Due to the massive 4-inch-thick flanges, it was quickly determined the effective preheat would require more than a cursory few seconds of flame application. The first column was properly preheated and welded. The next step was to inspect the weld after cooling to verify that no crack had formed.

The following morning, I returned to witness the weld inspection. Everything worked properly. The decision was made to preheat the joints and construction was to continue.

For several consecutive days I returned to the hospital construction site, often several times each day. No issues were reported. After several days, Joe volunteered that everyone was now satisfied and that I did not really need to visit again. Joe inquired if the visits and attention were an indication that I did not completely trust Joe to consistently make crack-free welds. I explained that I was very confident that all welds would be defect-free, but that I had alternative reasons to visit the hospital frequently. I explained that my wife had given birth to our first-born child, a baby girl who had been born via an emergency C-section with remarkable red hair and quite premature. She was six weeks early and weighed only 3 lbs. 15 ounces. The University of Connecticut Medical Center was the regional facility for high-risk neonatal intensive care. The baby was in the hospital neonatal intensive care unit, and the frequent visits were predicated on issues related to the baby rather than to the welding.

As they were headed to their vehicles, Joe to his truck and me to my car phone, Joe inquired if I liked my car phone. I told him that I was deeply afraid of the phone. Perhaps not the phone itself, but every ring caused fear. Each call could be news that the baby was doing well, or worse. Joe said, "We will need to see you tomorrow."

10 months later

In the summer of 1992, the car phone rang. The Women's and Brigham Hospital in downtown Boston was the location of a construction project, and something was wrong. Welds were cracking. The request was made that I cancel my plans and make an immediate visit to the construction site in Boston. I was perhaps 90 minutes away but could visit that morning.

I arrived to a rather congested construction site, an addition to the existing hospital. I visited the appropriate construction trailer office to announce my presence. I quickly surveyed the site. I inquired about the number of cracks. 27 of the 28 total columns had cracks, none of the columns were completely welded, and only the root passes had been made. The project was behind schedule. To move things forward, the engineer on site approved the pouring of floors prior to the completion of the column welds. I quickly suggested that they move out from under the 6 floors of concrete being held up only by cracked root pass welds on column splices.

A tense conversation quickly ensued. The hospital engineer, the steel fabricator, and the steel erector quickly wanted to claim compliance with all codes and standards and wanted to blame the manufacturer of the welding equipment and welding consumables, which was me. I asked for the steel Material Test Reports, and the welding procedures.

As they were waiting for the documents to be produced, around the corner strode an imposing figure. A 6 foot 8-inch-tall man dressed in welding leathers. I instantly recognized him. "Hello, Injun Joe," I said. "Shawn my boy, how are you?" he replied.

Joe explained to the group of engineers that we had seen this before on the Connecticut Hospital addition construction project. There were 4-inch-thick column flanges, dual-graded steel, and cracked columns. Joe also suggested that he had told everyone that they needed to preheat, but that nobody would listen because Joe was "just a dumb welder." Joe continued to explain that we needed to utilize rose buds and Tempil Sticks to verify the preheat, and that the welds could be made 100% defect-free. I added a few words related to the precise carbon equivalent of the subject steel columns and some technical details related to the metallurgy. I also inquired about the six floors of concrete already poured and the subsequent rigidity of the structure. Work needed stop above the ground level until columns welds could be made and verified.

As they headed to the vehicles after a stressful day, Joe to his truck and me to my vehicle with the car phone, Joe asked if he would see me in the morning. I handed Joe a business card with the car phone number and suggested that things were in capable hands. Further, if anything unusual were to transpire to please phone, but no, I didn't need to return in the morning.

Joe said, "Shawn my boy, I have to ask. Did the red-headed baby make it?"

Observations - the tale of Injun Joe

Why recant a story about structural steel welding from the early 1990s? I want to illustrate points via the telling of a tall tale; most of the stories are mostly true and accurate accounts. The following points are viewed as significant:

1) Consensus codes and standards are excellent works. They have been written with great effort and concern. They are intended to keep everyone from making avoidable mistakes. They represent the collective knowledge of specific matters or technologies that are appropriate to rational guidelines.

Mistakes are made when the prevailing codes and standards are viewed as the final word. Compliance can be achieved by ticking off the boxes but should never be utilized as a full and comprehensive understanding of the technology.

- What is right? The consensus codes and standards are great tools.
- What is wrong? The use of codes and standards does not permit the user to be uninformed, or to be overly reliant on the codes and standards. An understanding of the technology is still required. Mistakes are made when technology comprehension is abdicated.

2) Practitioners of the art (welders, laborers, workers) may have great historical knowledge or intimate understanding. They actually perform the work, and often they have great insight.

Joe knew that preheat prevents cracks. Joe knew that in Connecticut an issue was observed and a resolution was achieved. When the Boston hospital had a similar issue 10 months later, Joe knew how to resolve the issue. More specifically, when someone claims to be "just a dumb welder," You should be prepared to listen to the years of expertise they have to offer.

- What is right? Most people want to produce good work and have a sound concept about how to produce good quality work.
- What is wrong? Sometimes we fail to listen to the workers and this can be a catastrophic mistake.

Collusion with the Russians
January 1994

The nine-hour flight from New York to Moscow provided ample opportunity for contemplation and second-guessing. I had accepted the position of International Regional manager for Russia and the countries of the Former Soviet Union. The Berlin wall had fallen, and the Soviet Union had collapsed. The Cold War was over. President Reagan had called it the Evil Empire. The West, NATO, and the USA had viewed the Soviet Union as the primary threat to peace since the end of WWII. I was now headed to Russia, a world that few Americans had seen. My initial trip was scheduled for three weeks in duration. I was to visit Moscow, St. Petersburg (formerly Leningrad), and Volgograd (formerly Stalingrad).

The changing names of the cities must have been done with some contemplation. I wondered if this effort was made to appease the residents. Was "Leningrad" so profoundly negative in connotation that the people demanded a change, or perhaps was this just a marketing effort aimed at the rest of the world to state that communism was gone? Lenin never existed! Was "Stalingrad" so evocative of the Stalin era that the people wanted to erase the name from history, or was this a marketing effort to show the world that things had changed? The Russians were tricky folks with mysteries inside of enigmas wrapped in riddles. Why was I headed to Russia in January? I was not sent to wage war, but to try to sell welding products. Perhaps taking this assignment was not such a good idea. I spoke no Russian. I did not comprehend the Cyrillic alphabet. I could not even read a street sign.

My employer had secured office space in Moscow. The building had formerly been the location of the Ministry of Oil and Gas construction at 14 Zhitnaya Street between the current Ministry of the Interior and the Russian Central bank. This was a few blocks from the Kremlin. The entities that occupied the space had a history associated with oil and gas construction, particularly pipelines. Most of these entities were mere shadows of their former glory. The economy was in shambles. Very little construction was being planned nor completed.

Sometimes the phones in the Moscow office did work. You needed to schedule access to an international line in order to phone the USA. After the St. Petersburg leg of the trip, a few days were scheduled in the Moscow office. I made a request for an international phone line for late in the afternoon to correspond with morning office hours in the USA. I planned to phone Corporate HQ, where my new boss was based, and also phone home.

I elected to prioritize the call home ahead of the call to the office. I had no idea of the cost of international phone calls from my Moscow office to the USA, but it was my cost center, my budget, and my problem. No one in the office could provide an answer for the cost of a phone call. They only knew it could be complicated to get an international line. The phone call to home was placed and all was well, still almost two weeks before I would return home. I then phoned my office only to hear a lot of clicks, beeps, hisses, and crackles. The connection was made but was lost about 60 seconds into the call. The US-based office then knew I was alive as not much more was reported. The next available international line was two days in the future when I would be traveling to Volgograd.

I had gone from a car phone with reliable service 24 hours a day to the need to schedule an international line several days in advance. Was every conversation being monitored? I thought perhaps this was not a good career decision.

After the initial culture shock and some acclimation, I learned a few tricks of the trade. ATT Direct could be accessed via a local phone number in most cities, and with a pre-paid card, you could phone the USA for only a few cents per minute. This mechanism worked --- usually. I still assumed that perhaps every call was monitored. I had no evidence, just assumption.

The multinational oil companies had made investment commitments in various countries of the former Soviet Union. Russia, Kazakhstan and Azerbaijan were the most significant. Infrastructure was needed. This meant pipelines needed to be rehabilitated or newly built.

The VNIIST Institute was the entity that had a license from the Russian Government to certify or approve welding procedures, consumables, and technologies for pipelines. In the Soviet days, significant amounts of welding electrode had been imported to the Soviet Union from Sweden, Japan and Austria. Three international competitors had a history of clients and projects. My company, being American, had very limited history in the Soviet Union. However, they did have a solid global reputation.

The prevailing method of Pipeline welding for the entire Soviet Union was a manual stick electrode-based method utilizing a vertical up process and an electrode designation that was similar to an AWS E 7016 electrode for the root pass, and often for fill-and-cap passes.

E 7016 electrode is reasonably similar to an E 7018 designation, with the electrode coating being a bit different to produce a bit drying, stiffer arc, and perhaps a bit lower deposition rate. E 7016 was regarded as being susceptible to "piping porosity" or hollow bead in the root. The US tradition was an E6010 root pass, completed vertical down, and subsequent passes could be varied for specific metallurgical requirements.

My American Welding manufacturer did have multiple international electrode plants, and they did offer several trade name electrodes that met the E7016 classification, but none of these were made at the flagship plant in Cleveland, Ohio. The leading manufacturing plants for this specific type of electrode were in the Netherlands and Spain.

I had a decision to make. I could try to move the Russians to the US style E6010 root pass. I could try to sell the existing formulations of E7016 electrode. I could evaluate the cost and performance characteristics of the available E7016 formulation from my own company as well as the existing three international competitors, and perhaps convince the consumable R&D managers to create a new formulation. However, prior to any of these decisions I needed to evaluate the future instead of the past.

Who would make the ultimate decisions? Would the multinational oil companies insist on normal USA tradition E6010 methods? Would the Russians insist only on their E7016 methods? Would the Russians ultimately decide to import anything or insist on domestic production?

Multiple outcomes could result in little to no actual sales. Was a future market identifiable or potentially viable?

The logical path seems to suggest that it was appropriate to ask many questions and to try to locate the multinational oil company's management for the various countries of the Former Soviet Union. I also needed to locate the domestic oil and gas companies and the regulatory entities and ask questions. Many opinions were offered and conflicting responses were given.

Ultimately, the decision was made to try to create a new formulation for an E7016 electrode. We would try to create operator appeal characteristics as good as the best international competitor and meet or exceed all of the technical requirements.

The Russian welders preferred the Japanese product. They liked the arc characteristics, but the buying decision-makers often ignored the welders and bought the Austrian or Swedish products. Sometimes this purchase was based on price, and sometimes on other commercial concerns. Political complications were abundant.

After evaluations of the existing products, internal and competitive, my Cleveland-based company decided to formulate a new electrode. A couple of iterations were done and tested for mechanical results and operator appeal. I knew I could trust the mechanical test results, but the more subjective topic of operator appeal would involve actually welding on pipe. Pipe welders are notorious for having strong opinions, not always based on obvious observation. I had never been a particularly gifted pipe welder, but I was going to have to weld on actual pipe, on an actual joint, and evaluate the arc characteristics and make decisions. After several sessions welding both alone and with the very valuable help of several gifted welders, I decided that the Japanese product was still superior.

A meeting was convened at my company with the consumable R&D department. The four R&D participants aggressively lobbied that the product was excellent and that they had found success. I had some internal selling to conduct and needed to tell the formulators that the Japanese product had superior arc characteristics. I suggested that the product was in fact very good, but I had one concern. The Japanese competitor's product had a slightly better spray type transfer across the arc, while ours had a tendency to have the coating transfer in clumps. I suggested that it was almost as if the Japanese product had ground their coating a bit finer then the internal formulation. What would happen if my company ground the coating finer?

A silence fell across the room. They wanted approval and to move on to the next project. They did not want a never-ending development game. After a few seconds, one of the four offered that, yes, in fact they knew that the Japanese product had an electrode coating of smaller particle size than the internal formulation. He said the finer size would do nothing to help mechanical properties and would add perhaps 0.5 cents per pound to manufacturing costs. They suggested that the customer would not pay more than needed to meet the mechanical requirements arguing that cost control was vital.

After a discussion about the conditions in Russia including brown water, cockroaches, frozen fish and vodka for breakfast, it was agreed that a small batch of finer electrode coating particle size could be fabricated for evaluation.

It was time to take the newest formulation to Moscow for their evaluation. Dr. Natalia was in charge of the VNIIST institute welding lab. Dr. Natalia was not shy regarding opinions or advice. She possessed much knowledge of the international marketplace and the demands of Russia. It was to Dr. Natalia's lab that I transported the newest formulation. A large audience of spectators had assembled; somehow the American company working with the Russians was an interesting event.

Dr. Natalia had assigned her senior welder to the event. The man was about 60 years old, not a young person, and given the hardships of life in Russia in those days, 60 years old was considered a venerable age. He opened the hermetically sealed can of electrodes and removed one. He inspected it closely and commented that it was much better than Russian domestic electrode. The coating was still adhered to the steel, even after transport to Russia. He placed the electrode in the holder and addressed the pipe at the 6 o'clock position to begin a vertical up welding process. He struck the arc. After perhaps 30 seconds of arc time, he broke the arc, removed his welding helmet, and offered his assessment. Now I still couldn't speak any Russian so Dr. Natalia translated. She proceeded to tell me, "He says your development is no good!"

The International Regional Manager moved toward the pipe, crawled under to observe the weld bead. He stood up. He donned a pair of welding gloves and a welding helmet and indicated via hand signals that he wanted the electrode holder. The senior welder extended the electrode holder. I was going to weld. I addressed the pipe at the 6 o'clock position and struck an arc. I completed two electrodes of root pass. I then stood up and called the welder over to visually inspect the weld. The welder asked for the electrode holder. He placed his helmet on his head and returned to welding. He ran several electrodes worth of root pass. He stopped and suggested that maybe only the first electrode was bad. He would weld some more. He made some additional root pass beads and then some fill and cap pass beads. After a few minutes he declared that the electrode was in fact at least as good as the Japanese, but that welders would need to be careful about the first electrode out of the can!

Previously, a dinner had been scheduled with Dr. Natalia for that evening. This was a welcome event. It would not involve significant amounts of vodka.

I had some trepidation waiting for Dr. Natalia to arrive for the dinner. She was strong willed and not bashful. She would not sugar-coat her thoughts. My concerns revolved around the social norms and conventions. In much of the world, the business administrators administrate, the engineers engineer, the welders weld, and the workers work. The titular regional manager, me, was also the commercial guy, and also decided to weld in front of a large audience. This may have been an egregious faux pas. Dr. Natalia had not offered any immediate feedback after the welding had concluded earlier that day. Only that her people would use more of the electrode that afternoon and she would report the findings.

Dr. Natalia did not disappoint. Pleasantries and small talk were not exchanged. She took her seat at the restaurant table. She placed an elbow on the table and raised an index finger. Her eyes indicated that a most serious pronouncement was to be made. The table was hers and she commanded the table. A pause, a delay. The taiga in mid-winter waiting for spring. She proceeded to speak.

> *"What you did today, I must tell you, it was very impressive. The Japanese come to Moscow and the welder has a helper, the commercial guy has a guy who carries his bag, and the manager has a guy to carry his bag and an assistant. The Electrode developer is three people and three assistants, a dozen people or more arrive to weld with a new electrode. The Swedish people arrive with a team that has welders, welders' helpers, country managers, regional managers, business segment managers, maybe 10 people. The Austrians arrive and have about nine people. You Americans, you are the business manager, you are the commercial guy, you arrive and make your development work and actually weld! One guy does it all. You Americans are like us Russians, not afraid to work. I like that!"*

The elbow was then removed from the table and the index finger was lowered. Dr. Natalia continued: "My people like your development."

Soon the official approval was written for use within the Russian Federation. A few months later the commercial discussions began with the purchasing departments of the oil pipeline operator. By the mid-1990s the Americans and Russians were in solid collaboration on the sale of manual welding electrode for oil pipeline construction.

Observations - collusion with the Russians

Why include a story about Russian manual pipeline welding? As previously confessed, I like stories. The following points that are illustrated are important and relevant:

1) The pipeline industry in North America may feel colloquial or provincial. In reality the industry is global and opportunities abound.

2) The prevailing North American codes, standards, regulations, and technologies are the basis for much of the global pipeline industry.

3) The language may change, but the basic metallurgy, physics, chemistry and technologies remain the same. Comprehension and understanding of the basics is never a wasted skill.

4) The willingness to extend an effort is generally viewed as a great positive.

The Middle East on a hot day

The composite pipeline repair system had been developed in North America. The codes and standards were amended to include the technology. Soon the rest of the world began to display interest in utilizing this new technology. The Middle East was the world's leading oil production and export region, and natural gas pipelines were extensively utilized for power for desalination plants and chemical feed stocks. The installed base of pipelines was tremendous; much of the pipeline base was several decades old. This was an obvious commercial target for a composite pipeline repair company. The largest pipeline operator in the region had been only a minor customer for several years. The President and CEO of the composite company, me, had the opportunity to meet with the general manager of pipelines. At this meeting I inquired why the region's largest pipeline operator used only a few pipeline repair units annually. A straight- forward and honest answer was given. The pipeline operator brought in labor via ships from several countries, kept the laborers for six-month tours, and then sent them back home and a new group would arrive. Housing, food, and all related items as well as daily transportation to the pipeline work locations were provided. The widespread adoption of the composite repair method would entail the need for less laborers, which meant less drivers, less cooks, less staff for the camps. In short, it would require a change in established methods. The General Manager had the staff prepare an economic evaluation. The potential savings were only perhaps $40 or $50 million per year, and to achieve these savings much administrative work would be required. The $50 million in savings was not large enough to justify the change in culture that would be required. I suggested that where I came from $50 million per year was not a small amount and that I would continue with an effort to win over the General Manager. The General Manager in turn suggested that he wanted continued dialog, and that things may change in the future and to remain engaged with the sales effort.

A year later, at an industry event, the General Manager approached me and asked, "Will hydrogen diffuse through your device?" I indicated that I could not identify a specific test on the topic but was quite certain that hydrogen would diffuse through his composite. If the root of the question was about leaking hydrogen pipelines then, no, I could not claim that our product was a wonderful repair for hydrogen leaks. The General Manager indicated that hydrogen diffusion was beneficial. He continued on with a description of 10-meter-long welded type "B" sleeves, and said, "It is not good news when the Oil Minister calls at 4:00 AM and demands to know why his 42-inch oil export line that loads oil tankers in not operational." He went on to explain that the export line was down due to a stuck cleaning scraper tool. (Note: While in North America we call such tools "pigs," the cultural connotation of this term is not positive in certain geographic areas like the Middle East. In portions of the Middle East, they substitute the word "scraper" for "pig." The original use of a pipeline pig was in fact to scrape the inside of a pipe to remove interior buildup of undesirable materials.) He then went on to describe how the scraper was stuck under a welded steel sleeve. The technical people had determined that the blockage was due to an internal collapse of the carrier pipe wall which had been caused by the buildup and partial pressure equilibrium of hydrogen between the carrier pipe and the welded "type B" sleeve. When the pipeline was depressurized for operational reasons, the carrier pipe was deformed into its normal internal diameter. If he could stop the buildup of hydrogen in the annular space between the carrier pipe and the type B sleeve, the oil minister would not phone at 4:00 AM.

The General Manager issued instruction to change the custom and tradition of welded steel sleeves and to utilize the composite repair. The pipeline operator quickly became a very significant customer. Training was conducted for the field workers that would install units, technical staff to supervise, and a group of inspectors. Everyone had an interest in trouble-free high-quality field installations.

On a subsequent visit to the region, I asked to visit the site of an installation. I had a desire to verify that the field installations were being done properly. I asked if he could visit on the path to the airport that afternoon as I was scheduled on an early evening flight out of the region.

The Middle East can be rather warm during the summer months, and afternoon is typically the hottest part of the day. Rumors of plus 50 degrees Celsius were floated about. I thought that it could not be over 45° C (113° F) the day I visited the ditch.

The workers moved methodically but did keep moving despite the heat. My driver asked if he could remain in the vehicle with its air-conditioning while I was conducting my business. I observed the Inspector's truck running with the air-conditioning on. The inspector did emerge to inquire precisely why I was at the ditch, in the heat, and what I intended to accomplish. He soon retreated back to the cab of his truck.

I knew the instruction procedures very well, as I had personally been involved in a concerted effort to make the installation steps as clear and concise as possible. The installation was the last step in delivery of a trouble-free high-quality repair. I had taken special care to make the installation process and procedure as "idiot proof" as possible. The installation manual contained photographs of the significant kit components; the language was carefully selected to avoid potential misinterpretation of terms. An installer training curriculum was written and disseminated, and installers were required to pass both a "hands on" and written test. Similarly, inspectors had been trained with great care. Annual retraining and online exam requalification was an integral part of the program to ensure quality installations. A properly installed unit could not fail. The installation and inspection represented the final brush strokes of the effort.

When the driver had pulled up to the work location, he provided some translation for the foreman regarding the purpose of my visit. The foreman then translated to the workers. I understood well that my presence could impact the activities in the ditch. I verified that the material on site was appropriate for the task to be completed, that all components were accounted for, and that expiration dates for chemical components were not expired. All was well. I elected to back away from the ditch and let the workers continue their efforts, remaining vigilant, but from a distance.

The process was not complicated. A high modulus, high compressive strength filler material was used to fill any metal loss void or areas around any weld protuberances. This filler was methacrylate, filled for compressive strength, and activated by a rose or salmon-colored BPO paste activator. The amount of the rose-colored activator could be varied with external temperature, a bit less if it is hot like the Middle East, a bit more if it is cold like the Arctic. A pre-cured composite coil with strength member and resin components of specific architecture was the most visually significant component. This came from the factory with no field modification required. The composite coil was wrapped around the pipe with the filler placed in a wet uncured condition on the pipe surface. Then an adhesive was utilized on the surface of the pipe and between each layer of the coil. The adhesive was also methacrylate based and was activated by a blue colored BPO activator paste. The filler and adhesive activators were supplied in differently sized transparent pouches. The rose and blue colored activators and the different sized pouches were redundant precautions to avoid installer error. The final step of installation is that the coil is cinched or tightened to the pipe; excess filler and adhesive are extruded out from under the coil. The coil is taped in place until all is cured. The cure could be checked via hardness of the filler and adhesive typically in about 45 minutes, but perhaps faster in hot conditions.

I watched from a distance. The ambient temperature was taken and recorded. With this information the workers would know the appropriate amount of activators to utilize. The labels on the adhesive cans and filler cartridges included a chart of activator amounts required for various ambient temperatures. I did not involve myself in the selection of activator amounts, as the final hardness test would verify cure at the end of the installation process. The filler was opened, the activator amount selected, then they were combined and mixed. A second worked opened the adhesive and selected the amount of activator and mixed them following the written procedures. The activated filler was placed in the metal loss defects and around and welds. The adhesive was placed on the pipe surface, the coil was placed on the pipe, and adhesive was placed between every layer. The coil was tightened to the pipe and taped in place. Filler and adhesive extruded from under the composite coil. All appeared to be 100% proper and copasetic. I was pleased.

I then noticed some additional activity. One worker then collected the paint tray of unutilized extra adhesive. He also collected an extra pouch of the blue activator. He then poured the contents of an entire blue activator pouch into the small amount of remaining adhesive and quickly mixed them with a paintbrush. He then took this paint tray to the repair coil and painted the circumferential edges of the coil and the horizontal edge of the end of the coil. None of this activity was documented within the instruction manual.

I immediately knew both how and why this was being done. The addition of an extra pouch of blue activator would make the effective ratio of adhesive to activator perhaps in the range of 1:1. This would accelerate the exothermic reaction and the adhesive would cure within only a minute or two. The foreman waved to the inspector, who now left his air-conditioned truck, to check the hardness of the adhesive. The paperwork was completed, and the adhesive cured. They could now recoat the pipe and backfill the ditch.

The problem

The adhesive on the pipe surface and between each layer of the composite coil cannot be checked for proper cure; only the outside layer can be checked. By adding the extra activator, the inspection process was expedited. However, the effectiveness of the initial mix of adhesive could not be verified. Essentially, the workers had developed a method to maximize their marginal utility, get the inspector to sign the documents and depart, allow them to re-coat and backfill and then get out of the hot sun as quickly as possible. The integrity of the quality assurance/quality control aspects of the installation was violated.

I watched the installation and quickly had to consider the possibilities. If the workers were smart enough to understand how to manipulate the installation to maximize their own utility, while I was watching I might add, what might happen when nobody was watching? Perhaps they would utilize no filler at all, or no adhesive except for the visible external exposed surface. Perhaps no effective inspection was being done. Perhaps all previous installations were suspect at best and perhaps inadequate. The repairs are made to restore hoop strength. Inadequate repairs could potentially lead to uncontrolled releases, or explosions.

After some rather urgent discussions, the operator felt comfortable with the prior installations. It was determined that this crew was selected, as they were the smart installers, the good installers, and that the extraordinary steps of extra activator were only taken to expedite the inspection in hope that I would depart as well as the inspector. In addition, a series of random installations were evaluated. All were proved to be solid installations.

Observations - the Middle East

A) Rules, regulations, work instructions, and procedures are all key elements in the effort to have required tasks done properly and the desired result obtained.

B) Often several specific issues combine to create a problem. If the installers were not "so smart," or if the inspector was a bit more engaged, the potential issue would not have materialized.

C) When designing or engineering a product or process, it is prudent to consider how things could go wrong. It is also important to contemplate both how a poorly trained or inexperienced hand might make a mistake as well as how a very experienced smart hand might short circuit the integrated system of quality.

North America: A visit to a client's corporate headquarters

The Manager of Pipeline integrity was a very talented engineer. He was very competent, experienced and knowledgeable. He was active in the various industry organizations and significantly involved with the cutting-edge research and development efforts of the industry. He had made a decision to minimize the use of a specific composite repair product. I requested an opportunity to meet and discuss the decision.

The meeting began with multiple members of the pipeline integrity department; the manager was delayed for a few minutes due to other pressing obligations. The Manager of Pipeline Integrity soon joined the meeting. He was a technical person with a rather no-nonsense demeanor. The meeting was arranged to address the specifics of his decision to minimize the use of the company's products. As he was taking a seat in the conference room, the Manager wasted no time in getting to the point. "Every time we dig up your product it unravels and falls off the pipe. We can't accept that. We have left it in the Operating and Maintenance (O&M) language as approved, but we are not going to use it."

I had not been informed of any issues or failures. I was a bit surprised as the operator had been an early adopter of the technology and had been utilizing the product for over 15 years. I was prepared to address commercial issues; perhaps installation cost and the pipeline company's preferred contractor's installation fees. I was not well prepared for the claim that the product was not functioning well. I paused for a few seconds and asked, "Have you seen with your own eyes an installation that has unraveled or fallen off the pipe?"

The manager replied that he had received field reports but had not actually seen the phenomenon.

I then inquired of the other members of the integrity department in the meeting if had they seen the described issues with unraveling and falling off of the pipe. None had firsthand evidence. They did collectively suggest that a yard was only a few miles from the office, and at least two pipe segments had been deposited in the yard for further evaluation. I asked if I could visit the yard for a quick visual inspection, as I needed to know if I had a major systemic issue to address.

A visit to the pipe yard was approved for later that same day. Two lengths of pipe were quickly located, both perhaps 80 feet long and comprised of a couple of joined sections of pipe. Within these sections, several repaired areas were obvious.

A visual inspection of the repaired sections was completed; the repairs were unusual, not typical. A call was made back to the office to request permission to capture some photographs and video and to actually remove some wrapping material. Permission was quickly granted.

The product in question consisted of a procured composite coil. The architecture and color of the product are quite distinctive to the trained eye. The most typical installation involved a final step of the installation of the pipeline company's preferred anti-corrosion coating completely covering the composite repair area and tied into the original carrier pipe's coating. These installations were all similar and were not as expected. A liquid-applied epoxy field coating had been applied over the entire composite repair area and extended well onto the existing carrier pipe coating. In addition to this protective coating an additional product had been installed at each end of the composite repair. This extra coating extended perhaps three inches of linear length onto the composite repair and perhaps three inches onto the carrier pipe and over top of the previously applied liquid epoxy coating. This additional coating was in poor condition. It appeared to be a water-activated polyurethane and woven cloth combination. This extra coating had a high profile above the composite repair and the carrier pipe. This high profile would then result in maximum soil stresses on this extra coating. In several areas this extra coating could be removed by bare hand. After removal, the liquid applied epoxy field coating was in very good condition. The composite repair under this liquid applied epoxy coating was in excellent condition.

Video and photographs were taken and sent back to the office. An explanation of the findings was presented. The pre-cured laminated composite coil system, which was the subject of the meeting, was in excellent condition. The failed product was the secondary coating product applied. The intended purpose of this secondary protective coating was not identified. An unidentified wet applied field coating was installed and associated with the product I represented.

I did not earn back the business my company had previously enjoyed. The best agreement I could obtain was an agreement to remain in contact and to keep attempting to earn back the pipeline operator's business.

Observations - a visit to a client

1) "More" is not always "better." Adding a secondary or tertiary anti-corrosive coating as described in this story did not create an integrity treat or an actual pipeline issue. It did create the visual appearance after excavation of a problem.

2) Sometimes through no fault of your own, things turn out less well than you might hope.

The rest of the stories

I now have a new company and a new product. The Managers of Pipeline Integrity for the North American operators will be a significant target for technical explanations and validation discussions moving forward. This new venture represents a very large opportunity.

From the General Manager of Pipelines from the Middle East I learned that it is good to endeavor to make technology "idiot proof." It is also important to contemplate how to make technology "smart person proof."

There are wonderful people in Russia. There are wonderful people in the pipeline industry. Personal contact or business contact with individual Russian citizens can be extremely rewarding and educational. I hope that Collusion with Russians is not long remembered as a meaningful phrase.

The baby in the first story was born about six weeks premature. She weighed less than 4 pounds and spent about six weeks in the neonatal intensive care unit. Both the hospital addition and the baby have fared well. The Little Red Headed girl still has red hair, at the time of this writing she just wrapped up her two-year term as Chairperson of Young Pipeline Professional USA. She has worked for service providers and for pipeline operators and has decided to launch a new enterprise that focuses on pipeline integrity enhancement products.

Now the two big questions

I started this with two basic questions.

Q: What is right with the pipeline industry?

A: The people of the pipeline industry are what is right. Good people do good work. Around the globe, the pipeline industry has more than its fair share of high-quality people.

Q: What is wrong with the pipeline industry?

A: The most important metrics for pipeline integrity are not well communicated. It is possible to quickly obtain metrics for the financial performance of a pipeline entity. The organization type, MLP, "C" Corp or other form, existence of incentive distribution rights to the general Partner, distribution or dividend coverage, balance sheet leverage, earnings in various forms (EBIT or EBITDA), locations of assets that provides information on both supply and demand, etc. You can also quickly obtain information on governance as well as social and environmental evaluations from third-party rating agencies and investment firms. It is much more trouble ascertaining the status of asset integrity. Without integrity, the risk of the financial situation is not well defined. Trailing indicators, leaks or incident per barrel transported per mile is nice, but a prudent investor needs to comprehend the integrity of the system and the actual integrity philosophy to be applied. The industry needs a leading indicator, perhaps threats identified and removed per dollar invested. The age of pipeline assets and original construction information are informative, and the very diligent may locate data, but good integrity trumps asset age. Private equity has a growing interest while the multinational oil companies and super majors seem to have a diminished appetite for pipeline operations. The majors well understand reputational risk; private equity firms may have different timeframes and concepts.

Ten years ago, I had enough knowledge to invest in select pipeline operations with an eye toward the quality of the people within the integrity department. Good people worked hard to have on eye on the future threats and risks. Today this seems more difficult. The regulatory framework, capital structure and taxation systems for pipeline assets also present complications and challenges for individual investors.

Is the Industry investible from a financial standpoint? I currently find myself on the sidelines. A comprehensive discussion of these decisions seems beyond the scope of this chapter. It does seem reasonable to suggest that an investment in North American pipeline companies requires more analysis, investigation, and sophistication than in previous eras. The pipeline assets themselves should remain vital and economically important and viable well into the future. The risk to individual investors is that the available investment options may not provide a satisfactory long-term safe return on investment. The pipeline assets and employees will likely prosper, but an investor with no governance or management control might suffer negative surprises. An important caveat should be stated, with complication, complexity and perceived risks, opportunity may develop. It may be a mistake to avoid potential investments in the entire pipeline industry over the long term, but risk-averse prudent investors may want to remain cautious within the current context.

Is the industry investible from a career standpoint? I remain very optimistic and conclude that the pipeline industry is excellent as a career investment for children or grandchildren. I have had the privilege and good fortune to know many of the chapter authors from this compendium. Each is an advocate for pipeline integrity and works diligently to protect people, the environment and the pipe. Each has influenced dozens, hundreds, or thousands of others to endeavor to make things better. I'm confident in the belief that good practices, good mentoring, and a good attitude will always result in good results. The pipeline industry has an abundance of these.

The practice of pipeline risk management — advice to my younger self

Michael Gloven, PE

> *I'd provide very simple advice to young professionals to simplify the concepts of risk assessment and risk management. Find at least one mentor and ask them what lessons they've learned typically not found in a well-structured technical document on risk management.*

How did I get here?

Thirty years went by fast, and I can still recall moving from New Orleans after graduation to my first job as a pipeline engineer in Billings, Montana. I worked at a refinery with other young engineers, and our office had a wonderful view of a sour crude unit and tank farm. This was actually just going to be an interim job for me as I had other yet undefined ambitions in a large city. Well, over the years I've been fortunate enough to stay and continue to be part of the pipeline community with a career that's allowed me to hold more than 20 different positions, travel the world, start and lead two companies and make some great friends along the way.

When asked to write this chapter, I thought about what I might want to know as a young engineer or what advice I might give to someone just starting off in the world of pipeline risk management. To frame this in the context of this book "by God, if I were in charge," my advice would be to recommend younger engineers find at least one mentor and ask them what lessons they've learned typically not found in a well-structured technical document on risk management.

So, here are six lessons I might share with my younger self. Each lesson is organized into six concepts with links for further study. Lesson six is probably most important as it brings together the prior five lessons and covers the current trend of artificial intelligence and machine learning.

Lesson 1 - what's the real objective?

So, I'm on this risk team and our objective is to manage risk. Problem is, I really didn't understand what "risk" we were managing, and for that matter what "risk" really meant. At the time, it seemed like the objective was to enter data into this software, run some calculations, generate some colorful outputs and then inform management what we found. They sometimes used the results, but most of the time they already knew what to do, since they were older, wiser and had knowledge unknown to me as the young engineer.

Thinking back, I probably could have been more effective if I had a better understanding of the definition of "risk," since this was central to our objective and purpose of my work. It wasn't until years later I understood the concept of risk was more than a calculation of PoF x CoF. The most useful definition I found was actually through the ISO Risk Management standard where risk is defined as "a measure of uncertainty in the context of the organization's objectives." Hence, as obvious as it seems, understanding the objective was most important while the risk management practice was more about managing the uncertainty of achieving that objective.

Now, given that compliance was our primary objective, the risk practice was really then about the various processes, organizational structures and deployed technologies to manage the uncertainty around compliance. The ecosystem I participated in was purposed for this objective. Because I did not see the primary objective, my practice did not effectively align with the ecosystem.

The lesson then is to understand the true objective of the practice while looking for opportunities to be more effective. If you haven't done so already, check out the work initiated in 2015 through the PHMSA Pipeline Risk Modeling Work Group. The documents provide a good explanation of the state of pipeline risk models and supporting ecosystem. Further, within these documents it's interesting to note the typical objectives related to risk models, but still relevant to the overall risk management practice.

Fast-forward to today. We see compliance is still important, yet the industry is shifting towards a zero-incident objective. We might also observe that industry norms and regulations are starting to change while the risk practice is still being supported by a compliance-based ecosystem. This shift or transition will provide exceptional opportunities to those with the organizational courage to affect change in the practice. Emerging from this will be the future leaders in pipeline risk management.

All you've done is chisel all day! Do something useful, like helping your brother drag those rocks up the hill.

Figure 1. Innovation.

Table 1. Common uses of risk models.

	Operator Survey - Ranking of Risk Management (Modeling) Objectives
1	Rank Pipeline Segments by Risk
2	Identify Significant Failure Threats at Specific Locations
3	Identify High Risk Locations
4	Evaluate the Risk Against a Defined Acceptance Criteria
5	Evaluate Changes in Risk Over Time
6	Demonstrate Regulatory Compliance
7	Determine In-Line Inspection Intervals
8	Evaluate Mechanical Damage Prevention Strategies
9	Evaluate Risk Mitigation Strategies Associated with Road and River Crossings
10	Compare Pipeline Risk to the Risk Associated w\Other Assets within the Company
11	Select Excavations
12	Evaluate the Benefits of a Hydrostatic Test
13	Evaluate the Impact of Class Location Changes
14	Evaluate Pipeline Fitness for Service
15	Evaluate Pipeline Design Options
16	Inform Route Selection for New Pipelines or Pipeline Re-Route

Useful resources

Check out these resources to further explore the fundamentals of this lesson:

- ISO 31000 – Risk Management Principles and Guidelines
  https://www.iso.org/iso-31000-risk-management.html
- ISO 55000 – Asset Management
  https://www.iso.org/standard/55088.html
- IAM – The Institute of Asset Management
  https://theiam.org
- PHMSA Pipeline Risk Modeling Work Group
  https://www.phmsa.dot.gov/pipeline/risk-modeling-work-group/risk-modeling-work-group-overview

Lesson 2 - What's the point of understanding process?

Okay, I'm still part of this risk team, but really don't understand how my work is connected to the organizational ecosystem. In my role as a risk practitioner, data came from a vendor or another department, the risk rules were created by experts, results were generated by different software applications, and the resulting actions were somewhat disconnected from my carefully prepared outputs. I realize now I was supporting a sub-process of the larger process of risk management. I probably could have been more effective if I understood the basics of the overall process and how my actions affected other processes and, most importantly, the primary objective.

Process fundamentals are sometimes best understood as shown in Figure 2 PDCA (Plan, Do, Check, Act) from API 1173. Process is about managing the "who, what, where, when and how" of the work. If one of these five elements is missing or not performed as required, the process breaks down potentially resulting in an undesirable increase in uncertainty now or in the near future.

This is a long-lasting concept, and if you think about it, most or all uncertainty and risk has its roots in these process fundamentals. Thus, process is where uncertainty or risk is created, managed or mitigated.

Consider any type of threat or consequence and you'll see the uncertainty created was from one or more of these five elements. Understanding all work through the lens of process provides an effective approach to being successful in risk management. A good practice to understand root cause of any risk is to work through the full process using one of many process management applications or simply collaborating with stakeholders through a white board exercise.

Figure 2. API 1173 Plan, Do, Check, Act process.

Useful resources

Check out these resources to further explore the fundamentals of this lesson:

- PEX – Process Excellence Network
  https://www.processexcellencenetwork.com/
- APQC - American Productivity & Quality Center
  https://www.apqc.org/
- API RP 1173 – Pipeline Safety Management Systems
  https://pipelinesms.org/about/

Lesson 3 - maybe you should keep your Statistics 101 book

I sold all my books after graduating. Well, except for my nuclear engineering book which looked really cool on my bookshelf. Nonetheless, being in a risk practice requires fundamental understanding of data and results, which often benefit from statistical analysis. So, I should have kept my Statistics 101 book rather than buying the Idiots Guide to Statistics book I use today.

There are two areas of statistics that can be quite useful in pipeline risk management, descriptive statistics and inferential statistics. Both support an improved understanding of data and risk while also providing a good foundation for the emerging role of machine learning in pipeline risk management. More on that later...

In general, descriptive statistics is about understanding a population of data through measures of central tendency (mean, median, mode), measures of dispersion (range, variance, standard deviation) and non-normal and normal distributions (empirical rule).

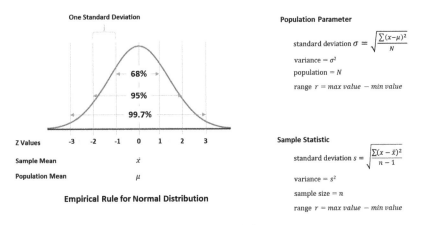

One Standard Deviation

68%
95%
99.7%

Z Values	-3	-2	-1	0	1	2	3
Sample Mean				$\bar{x}$			
Population Mean				μ			

Empirical Rule for Normal Distribution

Population Parameter

standard deviation $\sigma = \sqrt{\dfrac{\sum (x-\mu)^2}{N}}$

variance $= \sigma^2$

population $= N$

range $r = max\ value - min\ value$

Sample Statistic

standard deviation $s = \sqrt{\dfrac{\sum (x - \bar{x})^2}{n - 1}}$

variance $= s^2$

sample size $= n$

range $r = max\ value - min\ value$

Figure 3. Descriptive statistics.

If we harnessed data on every inch of pipeline for every second of the day, we'd probably have the knowledge or measures to understand and achieve a very low level of risk, as we'd be able to immediately respond to any unwanted variance in the process. However, this is not our current situation, so instead we infer knowledge of pipeline risk through data sampling.

Most, if not all, data important to risk is collected through sampling: an observation for a selected area of a pipeline is collected at a specific point in time to then represent a larger population. Inferential statistics is about using statistical methods to infer characteristics of the larger more complete population based on this sampling.

The sample data supports a belief about the integrity, condition or risk of a pipeline. Given that most data is provided through sampling, it's useful to qualify this data in terms of confidence or hypothesis testing. Confidence is most often expressed as a probability the belief is within a certain range. Hypothesis testing is the testing of a belief against a required level of significance and either rejecting or not rejecting the hypothesis.

Confidence intervals can inform the probability of a belief of a population parameter falling within a range. For example, through sampling you can calculate the probability of an assumed population average depth-of-cover actually falling within a range of values. If the assumed average does not fall within this range given a certain confidence, then an action might be to reject the assumption and improve the data set. As a practical example, if the belief is depth of cover is at least 36" and the 95% confidence level for the sample is 24"-32", then this belief may be rejected and the action might be to perform more thorough depth of cover surveys.

Hypothesis testing is a related method that allows you to test your beliefs thru sampling and criteria of acceptance. The criteria of acceptance is often expressed as a level of significance or probability the belief is true. Using the same example, if the desired level of significance is 5% and the sample calculates 3%, then the hypothesis would be rejected in favor of an alternative hypothesis.

The ability to measure the confidence of underlying risk data supports the assessment of data quality and measurement of the confidence of risk results. The technical learning to perform these two methods can be mastered through numerous on-line resources and courses. Check out the resources below and you'll have these techniques mastered in a few hours.

Useful resources

Check out these resources to further explore the fundamentals of this lesson:

- Khan Academy – Probability & Statistics
  https://www.khanacademy.org/
- An Introduction to Statistical Learning
  http://www.bcf.usc.edu/~gareth/ISL/
- Idiots Guide to Statistics
  https://www.amazon.com/Complete-Idiots-Guide-Statistics-2nd/dp/1592576346

Lesson 4 - be aware of mental errors

I like to think of myself as a rational person, but I'm not always one. The good news is it's not just me. We're all irrational, and we all make mental errors. For a long time, researchers and economists believed that humans made logical, well-considered decisions. In recent decades, however, researchers have uncovered a wide range of mental errors that derail our thinking.

The risk management practice can be quite data driven and logical. However, it's useful to be aware of your thinking as you work through the process and sample data, while understanding we are all prone to the following mental errors:

Survivorship bias

Survivorship bias can refer to our tendency to focus on what's most important, consequential or evident at the time and forget about what we believe is not important, but may actually be important. For example, we remember a particular coating and seam type leading to a failure, but don't remember 99.9% of pipe with the same coating and seam not failing. Survivorship bias is a heuristic or short-cut in our brains which allows us to make decisions quickly and efficiently. Being aware of our individual experiences and bias is helpful in being open minded when developing effective risk management strategies.

Confirmation bias

Confirmation bias refers to our tendency to search for and favor information that confirms our beliefs while simultaneously ignoring or devaluing information that contradicts our beliefs. It is not natural for us to formulate a hypothesis and then test various ways to prove it false. Instead, it is far more likely that we will form one hypothesis, such as a particular coating and seam type, assume it is true, and only seek out and believe information that supports it. Most people don't want new information. They want validating information.

The availability heuristic

The Availability heuristic refers to a common mistake that our brains make by assuming that the examples which come to mind easily are also the most important or prevalent things. We overvalue and overestimate the impact of things that we can remember, and we undervalue and underestimate the prevalence of the events we hear nothing about.

THE SURVIVORSHIP BIAS

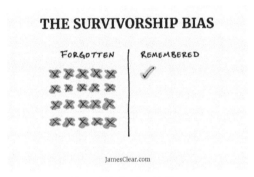

Figure 4. The Survivorship Bias.

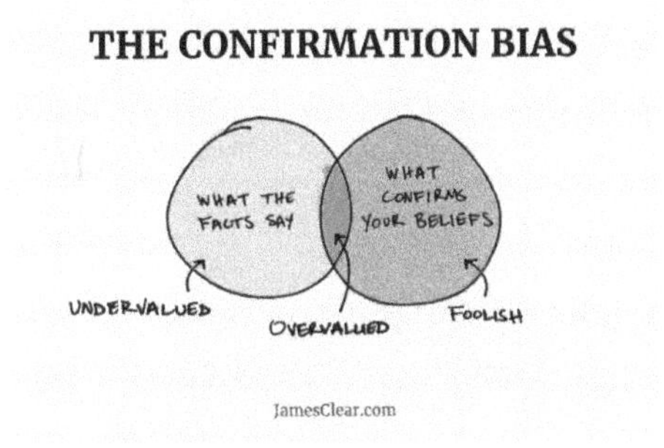

THE CONFIRMATION BIAS

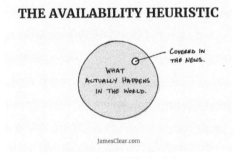

Figure 5. The Confirmation Bias.

THE AVAILABILITY HEURISTIC

Figure 6. The Availability Hearistic.

Where to go from here

Once you understand some of these common mental errors, your first response might be something along the lines of, "I want to stop this from happening! How can I prevent my brain from doing these things?" It's a fair question, but it's not quite that simple. Rather than thinking of these miscalculations as a signal of a broken brain, it's better to consider them as evidence that the shortcuts your brain uses aren't useful in all cases.

There are many areas of everyday life where the mental processes mentioned above are incredibly useful. You don't want to eliminate these thinking mechanisms. The problem is that our brains are so good at using these mechanisms — they slip into them so quickly and effortlessly — that we end up using them in situations where they don't serve us. In cases like these, self-awareness is often one of our best options.

Useful resources

Check out these resources to further explore the fundamentals of human thinking:

- Robert Cialdini – Influence, The Psychology of Persuasion
  https://www.amazon.com/Influence-Psychology-Persuasion-Business-Essentials-ebook/dp/B002BD2UUC
- Scott Adams – Win Bigly, Persuasion in a World Where Facts Don't Matter
  https://www.amazon.com/Win-Bigly-Persuasion-World-Matter-ebook/dp/B06X1DWK4Q/ref=sr_1_1?keywords=scott+adams+facts+dont+matter&qid=1562386690&s=digital-text&sr=1-1

Lesson 5 - seek out thought leaders

Early in my career I rarely wandered outside of my ecosystem. It wasn't until later I found excellent thinkers outside the domain of pipeline risk management who were thinking through and writing about the same concepts useful in our domain.

Of the many smart people writing about rare event management and understanding, two authors have devoted their professional lives to these studies and have written excellent books and articles related to risk management which can help improve your practice. If you haven't already read their work, you might find their content relevant and valuable in developing your own mental models about risk management.

Useful resources

Check out these authors:

- Andrew Hopkins - Disastrous Decisions – The Human and Organizational Causes of the Gulf of Mexico Blowout
https://www.amazon.com/Disastrous-Decisions-Organisational-Causes-Blowout/dp/1921948779
- Nassim Taleb - Incerto (Black Swan, Fooled by Randomness, Anti-Fragility, Bed of Procrustes, Skin in the Game)
https://www.amazon.com/Incerto-4-Book-Bundle-Randomness-Antifragile-ebook/dp/B00K5190LE/ref=sr_1_1?keywords=nassim+taleb+incerto&qid=1562386878&s=digital-text&sr=1-1

Lesson 6 - understand the role of machine learning

This last lesson ties together the previous lessons by presenting machine learning practices in the context of improving pipeline risk management. This is not so much a lesson as a set of ideas for improvement and professional learning.

At a fundamental level, machine learning is about finding useful patterns in data and using these patterns to support future predictions. The machine learning practice is quite mature in many areas, but is also a wide, complex and rapidly progressing field. If you're relatively new to machine learning there are numerous on-line resources available, and you can check out the resource links below to take a deeper dive into the subject. For the purposes of this lesson we'll focus on just a few key concepts particular to pipeline risk management.

We can safely say that today we're inundated with data, often too much to fully process, understand and validate. Continuous assessments and inspections, one-call data, public GIS data, historical asset records and the rapid development of satellite technology can be overwhelming. In fact, the number of new satellites being launched will soon provide hyperspectral digital data across most of the earth's surface every few hours.

This is where machine learning methods can help. Some of the methods have been around more than 100 years, including fundamental techniques such as ordinary least squares, logistic regression, Bayes theorem and Shannon's entropy. These methods are mature, validated and well understood and play key roles in machine learning. The machine learning process can help determine what is important, influential and useful.

Today, it may seem odd that machine learning methods don't play more of a key role in risk management. We often create risk rule sets (patterns) to support mitigation decision-making. These sets are based on opinions of well-intentioned experts with their personal experience bias often supported by data of unsubstantiated quality. We then take these rule-sets of questionable quality, which are rarely validated, and reapply them back to the data of unsubstantiated quality. This appears to be a circular process of decision-making supported through survivorship and confirmation biases.

Let the Data Speak – The improvement idea is to let the data speak "prior" to filtering it by expert or data manipulation bias. Since machine learning is based on data, method selection and parameter optimization to minimize error, the results can provide useful insights into data quality, threat based rule-sets and mitigation effectiveness. The process, methods and tools are available to do this, and the results could only add value to the practice.

Many current risk approaches may be classified as "traditional," that is they are a mix of deterministic and expert-biased formulations or rule sets. Often the traditional approach applies rules to data that have no measures of confidence, and thus the risk results are not validated with levels of confidence. Maybe this satisfies the objectives of compliance and prioritization of assets for increased scrutiny, but the results may be limited in their ability to measure the effectiveness of mitigations, measure the actual quality of data and generate monetized risk values to support mitigation decision-making.A data-driven machine learning approach flips the early steps of the process where rules are created by data that are then reviewed and acted upon by domain experts. The added value of data-driven, learned models is there is an associated performance vector substantiating the validity of the model, expressed as an expected error, sensitivity, specificity, etc. This is rarely available in traditional approaches as a way to inform the practitioner of model validity. Further, implicit in a data-driven model is validation and measurement of the historical effectiveness of controls which would seem to be useful in any risk management program.

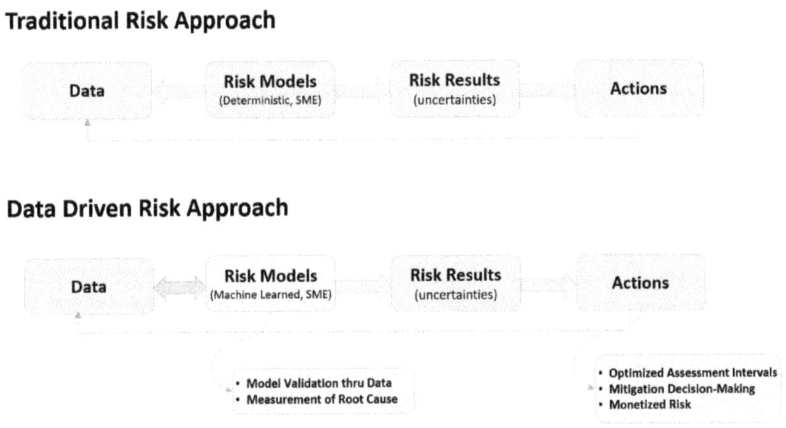

Traditional Risk Approach

| Data | Risk Models (Deterministic, SME) | Risk Results (uncertainties) | Actions |

Data Driven Risk Approach

| Data | Risk Models (Machine Learned, SME) | Risk Results (uncertainties) | Actions |

- Model Validation thru Data
- Measurement of Root Cause

- Optimized Assessment Intervals
- Mitigation Decision-Making
- Monetized Risk

Figure 7. Comparison of Risk Approaches.

Examples of Informed Validation - Machine learning methods inform the relationship of historical data to targets of interest, and this information reveals how well underlying data could predict the target. Consider the following in the context of threat assessments:

The regression coefficient of determination (R^2) in machine learned linear regression informs the practitioner of uncertainty of data explaining the target. A data driven learned R^2 of 35% indicates the underlying data only explains 35% of the target while 65% is unexplained. Is this 65% acceptable? Where?

Shannon's entropy may be used to measure threat susceptibility and is often the basis of decision-tree learning models. Let's say the current level of data collected supports a data-driven model specificity (false positive %) and sensitivity (1-miss %) of 10% and 80%, respectively. This means out of 100 predictions you'd expect to have 10 false positives (go look, nothing found) and 20 misses (didn't look, but something is there). Is this acceptable? What's the cost of the false positives vs. the misses, and is your organization ready to accept this risk?

These examples illustrate just two of many ways to assess your data "as-is." The results are data-driven. They represent what your data is currently telling you. This information could be quite strategic in your practice, as you will be able to measure the quality of your data and performance of your models, which then supports effective decision-making regarding investments in developing your internal ecosystem and mitigations.

If you're curious about the value of machine learning, check out the resources below. They'll get you started in the fundamentals.

Useful resources

Numerous courses and on-line resources are available through a simple on-line search. The Andrew Ng course is a must take for understanding the fundamentals.

- Coursera Machine Learning Course – Andrew Ng
  http://bit.ly/33D7NcK

- Machine Learning Guide - Audio Podcasts
  http://ocdevel.com/mlg

The challenge of effective technology transfer in the pipeline industry

Bill Amend, P.E.

 *BY GOD, IF I WERE IN CHARGE...*

> 1. *I'd challenge the researchers to more effectively convert their new information into useable tools for the end-user,*
> 2. *Have industry organizations do a better job of tying together and summarizing all the new information related to specific topics, and*
> 3. *Promote the continued importance of subject matter experts (despite everyone having access to the wealth of information on the Internet).*

I was in corporate metallurgical engineering staff positions for liquid and natural gas pipeline operators for about 26 years, followed by another 14 years as a subject matter expert (SME) for engineering and pipeline integrity management service providers. In those various roles I have been both a user and an author of new technical information for the pipeline industry. One of my roles as both an operator and later as a service provider has been technical training and my exposure to a large number of pipeline operators and service providers has given me some unique perspectives on how the industry generates, distributes, and applies new information. In this chapter I discuss the on-going challenges associated with information management and specifically, the transfer of new pipeline-related technical information from those who develop it to those who can use it.

While information technology has improved, thus presumably making dissemination of new information easier, the rate at which new technical information is developed has also hugely increased. Even if a technical topic is narrowly defined, it can be a full-time job for a user to find and digest all pertinent, new technical information, let alone determine how to convert it to a format easily understood by and properly applied by end-users within the pipeline company. The related challenges can be divided into two broad areas:

1) How is new information disseminated by the sources and discovered by the users?
2) What challenges exist in the timely application of new information by end-users once it is discovered?

This chapter breaks both of those into multiple related questions or challenges and addresses them individually.

The scope of the problem Part 1: Information overload

New technical information pertaining to the pipeline industry is generated and disseminated by the sources at an overwhelming pace. By spending about an hour on internet searches I was able to find information on the following sources of new information for the industry; there are no doubt more that could be discovered in a more exhaustive search:

- 21 regularly published journals with technical information about pipelines (and another twelve journals that focused mainly on nontechnical aspects of pipelines and the oil & gas business)
- 15 industry associations that related to pipelines, including at least five of which author, publish and update widely referenced standards applicable to pipelines

- 3 membership-based organizations who primarily conduct group-sponsored pipeline technology research projects (PRCI, NGA/NYSEARCH, and GTI)
- 22 different technical conferences or symposia for North America in 2019, primarily or at least partially focused on pipelines
- A very large number of training workshops and webinars aimed toward improving the technical competency of pipeline industry staff. These are offered by various technical associations, individual service providers, material and equipment manufacturers, research organizations and their contractors, and organizations that specialize in technical training, technical symposia and workshops.

Those numbers exclude events, organizations, and publications that mainly relate to pipelines in other parts of the world, as well as journals which have only occasional relationships to pipelines. For example, although some content might be potentially insightful for pipeline technical staff, the list omits failure analysis publications in which pipeline failures are only occasionally discussed. The list also excludes the service providers who perform pipeline technology research through joint industry projects (JIPs) or group-sponsored projects (GSPs) as a secondary area of focus compared to their primary technical service offerings. In North America those service providers include but are not limited to BMT Fleet technologies, C-FER, DNV GL, Kiefner Associates/APPLUS, and Stress Engineering Services.

A closer look at selected sources further reveals the magnitude of the new information tsunami. For example, PRCI divides their research into eight subject areas. The PRCI website describes 22 simultaneous research projects currently under contract or in progress for a single subject area (Design, Materials, and Construction committee) at: https://www.prci.org/Research/ProgramsProjects.aspx?technical-committees=48_315.

The PRCI website also includes 1,394 final reports for various research topics, with 100 of those reports being published between January 1, 2018 and March 4, 2019. In another example, a PHMSA webpage (https://primis.phmsa.dot.gov/matrix/FinalReports.rdm) lists over 230 final technical reports (downloadable for free) for PHMSA-sponsored pipeline R&D projects issued since 2005, plus, there are additional technical reports available from the PHMSA website here: https://primis.phmsa.dot.gov/matrix/Library.rdm

I believe, the inability to successfully address technical challenges in a safe, cost-effective, and technically defensible manner is not always caused by a lack of technical information. My experience in my involvement in these organizations shows the bottleneck in problem solving is often in technology transfer. Technology transfer is the process of efficiently disseminating new information in a way that makes it readily discoverable, and then translating the newly available technology into improved engineering or operations and maintenance (O&M) practices. In the organizations I've worked for (both operator and consultant) the old paradigm was that an organization needed very smart people who knew a lot of facts and who could use those facts in problem-solving. Their expertise was gaged by how many file cabinets full of reports, conference proceedings, and pages torn from journals they had saved and filed. With the volume of new technical information being generated by large numbers of different sources, it becomes impossible for the SME to be the "knower of all facts" relevant to a technical topic, unless the topic is very narrowly defined.At the pace of information development today, if a company wants to depend on staff who know all the details about a topic, it means they will need to hire a lot more SMEs to cover the range of topics applicable to a pipeline technology and engineering. I do not believe that is practical or likely. Therefore, rather than depending upon a staff member to know everything about a topic, the new key to success may be emphasis on having staff who are able to efficiently *find* new information on an as-needed, when-needed basis, and convert that new information into usable solutions.

Where do we start in the process of information discovery and management?

Success in technical transfer hinges, at least in part, on having the right human in the right role. In my opinion, pipeline operators need to have technical staffs comprised of employees who really like engineering and problem solving and are willing to make the long-term commitment to developing into an SME. They should like finding and learning new technical information.

Whenever I talk about the continuing need for SMEs, a common response is along the lines of "Why do I need an SME if I have generalists who can do a web search for anything they need?" The answer comes from a conversation I had with a manager who wears a second hat as an SME. He said one of his more "generalist" engineers had located a published research report that appeared to answer a current technical challenge. However, this generalist told him "I have read this twice and still don't understand it." In the absence of those SME resources, companies become increasingly dependent upon consultants who will not have the same familiarity with company-specific assets and operations as in-house staff have.

The pipeline companies need to find the right people then foster technical staff development by making sure their new staff members have three opportunities including:

1) **Participation in industry committees**: This fosters networking, benchmarking, and better understanding of the "sausage-making process" that comprises the development and revision of technical standards and the development of research road mapping. Early in my career my manager insisted that every member of his staff attend every local monthly NACE meeting and go to the annual NACE convention and be active on the NACE standards committees. I was in my 20s and not a fan of going to monthly dinner meetings with a bunch of "grizzled veterans" of the industry, but boy, did I meet a lot of people who would become valued resources in the future.

I also learned a lot about corrosion control technologies that were only peripherally related to my personal interest in oil & gas metallurgy and related corrosion issues. Exposure to those other technologies through those NACE activities broadened my understanding of the problems and solution options for corrosion in the oil & gas industry.

2) **Intimate knowledge of what the challenges are in field operations**: If you don't know from first-hand knowledge what the problems are, you don't know what solutions to look for. I asked a company materials engineering/materials sourcing SME how he would develop new staff who needed to become his eventual replacement. He said the key first step was to spend significant time in operations with the end-users. Find out what problems they face, then develop a list of priorities to address.

3) **Guidance in technical development**: This does not just mean a line item on a performance plan. This means sitting down with the junior technical staff before they go to a symposium, workshop, or conference and setting expectations about what they will try to learn there. My first manager (a true SME in the field of pipeline corrosion) reviewed every conference agenda before I went and told me which presentations were likely to be the best based on his knowledge of the presenters and the subject matter. A generic engineering manager will be less able to successfully do that than a true SME. Expectations should include the junior staff summarizing what they learned and then sharing it with other technical staff. Short presentations in a "lunch 'n learn format" are great, but if nothing else, the summaries should be posted to a shared computer drive that makes the information readily accessible to all in the future.

However, the client companies with whom I deal regularly seem to be trending toward fewer true in-house SMEs and greater reliance upon their increasingly "generalist" engineers finding answers to questions and problems as they occur. That means the operator is either increasing their reliance upon service providers who have true SMEs, or they are depending upon their "generalist" in-house technical staff to have great skill at (and interest in) finding, digesting, and then applying complex technical information.

I recently met separately with two former co-workers who have gradually become true SMEs (albeit with some direct reports as well) at their respective pipeline companies. They both told me nearly identical tales of woe. Finding entry level engineering staff who want to be SMEs is very difficult. The entry level technical employees most often want to be generalists and move around the company to different positions with the objective of finally becoming a manager. The problem is further compounded by Human Resources departments who consistently fail to understand the personality traits often associated with wanting to be an SME. As I was told by the one SME, HR keeps rejecting the introverted candidates who actually LIKE to focus on grinding out numbers and interpreting complex research results. They did not fit the corporate vision of the socially acceptable, gregarious workforce. He told me "Those rejects are exactly the people I need!"

Does the needed information or technology exist?

An obvious first step in the technology transfer process is that the user must become aware that the new information exists. How is that accomplished?

Let's assume that a company has technical staff who are responsible for finding solutions to problems not already addressed in the company standards and Operations and Maintenance (O&M) manual. How will they find helpful technical resources? Membership-based organizations such as R&D organizations and various industry associations use e-mail to alert their members that the organization has published, or is working on, new information of potential interest to the user. Assuming the user does not allow those messages to be mistakenly routed to a spam message folder, the user will know that something is available for download or on-line review.

The bigger challenge is to remain aware of new information origi-
nating at other sources, such as the myriad of available technical journals, books, conferences, workshops, webinars, and symposia. As noted
in Table X, some formats are commonly indexed and discoverable by a
simple internet search, while others may not be. In some cases, the information might not always be listed in the results of a Google search,
but can be discovered by searching the on-line index of publications
or documents maintained for download (for free or for sale) by the
publishing organization. NACE International, PRCI, and INGAA are
examples of organizations which list available technical documents on
their websites. Some manufacturers and service providers also maintain indices of available reports or other resource documents they have
authored on their websites. Examples include, but are not limited to,
Keifner & Associates, C-FER Technologies, and Engineering Mechanics Corporation of Columbus.

The agendas for technical conferences and symposia are generally
posted on the internet far in advance of the event. Most event hosts will
list, and in some cases provide abstracts for, the technical presentations. Copies are typically available from the conference organizers after the conference, or the author can be contacted directly and may be
able to provide information similar to that presented at the conference.

There is a downside to relying upon checking the Internet for descriptions of technical conferences and the related proceedings, or in
checking websites of individual associations or service providers or
manufacturers. Success is dependent upon the user knowing who the
most likely sources of needed information will be and requires separate
visits to many websites.

Alternatively, those who need awareness of the new technical
information can use various search engines that to find information
applicable to pipelines. Wikipedia (accessed March 7, 2019) lists 39
English-language searchable academic databases and search engines
which appear to be potentially applicable to pipeline applications (i.e.,
those related to science, engineering, multi-disciplinary topics, technical journals, etc.). Of those, 25 are indicated as having some free functionality, while the others are subscription based. Some can be set up

to send e-mails alerting the user to the addition of a new article or report that meets predetermined search criteria. Since different search engines use different databases, it is highly likely that different search engines will produce different results. For best results, users should consider using multiple search engines and anticipate having to tinker with key word combinations to obtain the desired coverage.

How is new information transferred from the originator to the end-user?

In my experience, as a researcher, a trainer, and a consumer of new technical information, I have observed several ways that the originator or author can make their new developments or discoveries accessible to other subject matter experts and end-users. Each information format and information transfer sequence model have advantages and limitations and no single method is always the most effective, nor is any single method guaranteed to reach the most users. One model for transferring new technology to end-users is illustrated in Figure 1. In that illustrated model, the effectiveness of the transfer is at least partially related to how many of the options (indicated by the dashed lines) are included. For example, I have found that peer review, while generally focused on technical accuracy, can also identify opportunities to make the content more readily understandable by end-users and more adaptable to pipeline company operational needs.

I have watched technology transfer evolve over my 40 years of experience. The types of information presentation formats have changed over time, reflecting technological advances that enable new formats, such as webinars or electronic publishing. Table 1 summarizes some of the advantages and limitations of the various information distribution formats from the standpoint of an end-user.

One consideration that I find is often overlooked is the format of the information. The format can influence the effectiveness of information transfer and comprehension by the user. Some people learn better by visual inputs. Some users learn better via audio, and particularly when the format supports interaction between the information provider and the information user. The Socratic method of learning is quite difficult or impossible to implement when the information is only presented in a static, written format. Therefore, the effectiveness of technology transfer can be different whether the information is provided as a written document (e.g. books and reports in either paper or electronic format), or as a presentation format that combines visual aids with audio. Examples that combine visual and audio formats include live or recorded webinars and live workshops or presentations at conferences and symposia.

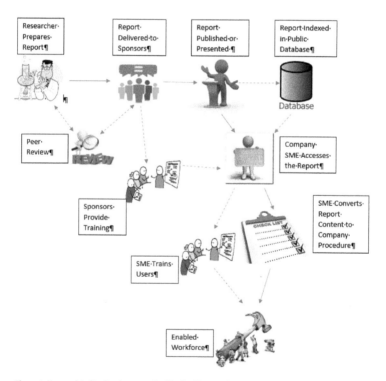

Figure 1. One model of technology transfer. (Dashed lines indicate steps that are sometimes omitted.)

Technology has allowed information delivery to become much more of a multimedia experience capable of holding a participant's attention. Improvements in computer graphics have made it easier to incorporate video into presentations. Many websites now include information included in both visual (including video) and audio format. Early in my career we all tried to convey information by showing a series of overhead transparencies or 35mm slides. Those formats eventually gave way to PowerPoint presentations. The use of projectors combined with laptops has enabled presenters to show information in a variety of formats (text, photos, tables, graphs, embedded videos) and swap between various software applications, e.g. between PowerPoint and Excel, or between PowerPoint and specialized technical software, to illustrate certain concepts or procedures. Knowing the audience is key to picking a presentation format. Younger staff will expect to see a multimedia presentation supplemented with a lot of interaction with the presenter and exercises that include collaboration with other attendees, if you intend to hold their attention.

Table 1. Summary of Characteristics of Various Information Distribution Formats.

Format	Advantage for User	Disadvantage for User
Informal networking	Highly interactive Flexible formats Low cost Facilitates easy benchmarking	Typically, no supporting materials for future reference Information not usually peer reviewed or formally referenced; reliability of information is less established
Web-based discussion forums	Low cost Facilitates easy benchmarking, assuming other participants respond Some current and past internet discussion forum topics are discoverable by web search May be useful for getting ideas for further investigation using more authoritative sources	Uncertain or inconsistent quality of comments and answers; inconsistent peer review Some types are not discoverable by web search

Table 1 continued

Format	Advantage for User	Disadvantage for User
Books, reports, conference papers; paper format	No computer required for access Generally peer reviewed or professionally edited Includes publications from pre-computer age No travel required Accessible at user convenience May be easier to make notes on the paper copy than in an electronic copy.	Not interactive Limited search capability; Requires scanning or copying to share Requires significant storage space Not accessible by computer No Q&A opportunity May be higher cost than the same product in electronic format
Journal articles	Sharable Generally peer reviewed or professionally edited Discoverable by web search No travel required Accessible at user convenience May be available in paper and electronic format	Not interactive Extent of detail varies from being a broad overview to being narrow and detailed in scope; may require supplemental information to be useful Not optimum for users who prefer learning by audio Paper copies have greater storage space requirements
Reports; electronic format	Sharable (unless locked) Generally peer-reviewed or professionally edited Often discoverable by web search No travel required Accessible at user convenience	Not interactive Not optimized for learners who prefer listening as opposed to viewing No Q&A opportunity Can sometimes have a long lag time between development and approval/publication
Conference papers; electronic format	Sharable (unless locked) Generally, peer-reviewed Lower expense than live conferences or live training; no travel required Accessible at user convenience	Not interactive May be less comprehensive than a full report, book or training course May not be discoverable on web search

Table 1 continued

Format	Advantage for User	Disadvantage for User
Classroom training, live conferences, symposia, or workshops	Highly interactive Networking opportunities No in-office distractions Often accompanied by a written format of the same information; may include supplemental reference materials Often accommodates both visual and audible presentation formats	Often requires significant travel time and expense Quality and completeness of reference materials that support the live presentation can vary Requires users to be available at scheduled time Presentations may not be discoverable on web search
Webinar – live	Somewhat interactive; generally allows Q&A No travel time or expenses compared to attending live conferences or symposia Generally low cost or free Short time requirement Accommodates both visual and audible presentation formats May address either details about a narrow scope, or be an introduction to a broad topic	Potential for in-office distractions May or may not result in a permanent record for future reference Often not discoverable by web search Requires user to be available at scheduled time No "Pause/rewind/fast forward" Not discoverable in web search after completion (unless recorded)
Webinar- recorded	Generally, a short time requirement for completion Generally low cost Accessible to user at convenient times No travel time or expenses compared to attending live conference/symposia presentations Accommodates both visual and audible presentation formats May allow "pause/rewind/fast forward" and repeated view of areas of interest May be less expensive than other forms of training May address either details about a narrow scope, or be an introduction to a broad topic May be discoverable by web search	Not interactive Potential for in-office distractions May or may not result in a permanent record for future reference May not allow Q&A

To support the management of change (MOC) process, computer-based training (CBT) is now capable of delivering information at a speed that is controllable by each learner. CBT can also include in-course assessments that track comprehension and verify and document the user's ability to properly apply the new information. Those who need to use the new information are less reliant on traditional classroom instruction, which traditionally takes a "one size fits most" approach to information delivery and the ability of an "average" recipient to absorb new information.

A few of the information transfer formats from Table 1 warrant further discussion.

Informal networking is one form of technology transfer that has probably been around since there has been information worth exchanging. Early in my career in the 1980s I was supporting refining operations in addition to various oil & gas production and pipelining operations. In the greater Los Angeles area there were several refineries operated by various companies who shared some common technical challenges. There was an informal Refinery Information Exchange group that met for dinner occasionally on a defined schedule. There were no formal presentations, but everyone had an opportunity to propose technical topics for discussion. It was an outstanding resource for informal benchmarking and an opportunity to learn from some of the more experienced professionals. Everyone knew each other and their qualifications. No formal minutes were taken or distributed, and everything was off the record, but it effectively distributed new information about new best practices. Note that this was before e-mail that eventually made it easy to share ideas among peers, although the "permanent written record" of e-mail can sometimes influence the extent to which issues are freely discussed.

The closest modern equivalent might be the networking that occurs at lunches, breaks, and receptions at various conferences, workshops, and related industry events held during the year. In fact, some participants note the opportunity for informal networking as one of the key advantages to attending such events. Some conferences and workshops have adopted a somewhat more formalized approach by hosting "discussion panels." The next closest facsimile might be the exchange of information through electronic bulletin boards/discussion forums such as those sponsored by some groups on LinkedIn, or at Eng-Tips. com. For example, members of LinkedIn can join discussion groups exemplified by these pipeline-related titles:

- Pipeline Integrity Management Group
- Slurry Pipeline Group
- Pipeline Data Management Group
- Oil & Gas Pipeline Safety and Industry Group
- Pipeline Regulatory Issues Group
- Pipeline Inspector Group
- Pipeline Design Engineer Group
- Pipeline Corrosion Control Group
- Pipeline Coatings Group
- Pipeline Welding Group
- FERC Pipeline Networking Group
- Pipeline Professionals Group
- Underground Utilities Damage Prevention Group
- API 1169 Certified Pipeline Inspectors Group
- Pipeline Pigging Group
- In-line Inspection Group

Some manufacturers also sponsor discussion forums on their websites, for example Miller Electric Mfg. hosts a discussion forum for welding issues.

A key disadvantage of most internet-based forums is that the experience and qualifications of the respondents are often unknown. The user is left to try to discern the defensibility of the answers based on the presence or absence of conflicting responses if the reputation of a specific respondent is not known. It is generally considered unwise to rely solely on discussion forums for technical answers. However, in my experience, responses in discussion forums can point a user to some previously unrecognized options and those can then be researched in more detail using other resources.

The second format of technology transfer that deserves more discussion is technical reports. Often these are detailed descriptions of research findings, conclusions, and recommendations that can stretch well beyond 100 pages and include extensive text, equations, captioned photographs, tables, and graphs. While they can provide an excellent resource for development or defense of a new procedure or practice, they seldom are readily transferable into O&M Manual content or a procedure usable by field personnel. They require that a subject matter expert (SME) within the user's company review the document, determine the applicability to a company-specific situation, identify any conflicts with regulatory limitations, and distill the key content into the company's procedure or policy document format. Those formats are often characterized by brief introductory text describing the scope, applicability, and boundary conditions, followed by a series of short bulleted or numbered statements representing the "recipe" for application. As a result, in the technology transfer process 100 pages or more of complex report is distilled into a few (or occasionally several) pages of new or edited procedure for use by end-users within the company.

The company SME is, in that scenario, the key to timely and successful implementation of the new information. In the absence of an in-house SME, the company becomes dependent upon a consultant. The consultant may or may not know the details of the company's existing procedures and the daily challenges their staff encounters in field operations. The expert's role is complicated not only by the requirement that they be able to reduce complex reports to usable formats, but also by the need to follow the company management of change (MOC) requirements and the need to effectively roll out the new procedure or policy to the end-users within the company. Effective translation of the report to new company procedures can be thwarted by any of the following:

1) Failure of the SME to recognize the existence of the report (or similar technical document) and its applicability to their pipeline company: In view of the number of sources of potentially new information summarized in the section above ("The

Scope of the Problem; Information Overload) it is a challenge for an SME to remain up-to-date on all potentially applicable new reports or other documents

2) Failure to review and process the report in a timely manner so that delay in conversion to company procedure format is minimized: With typical workloads that include time-sensitive tasks, it is difficult to ensure that new information, once identified, is consistently obtained and reviewed and distilled into Company Procedure format in a timely manner.

3) Incomplete understanding or misunderstanding of the report by the SME. The report authors (or sponsoring organization) need to convey the information in an effective manner, perhaps by supplementing the report with a workshop. There is more likelihood for error in implementation when the SME does not interact with the report's authors and has not had the benefit of participating in discussions of the report via workshops or live presentations or webinars by the authors.

4) Unresolved conflicts in similar information derived from different sources, for example reports on the same topic that originate from different sources and which reach different conclusions. Independently conducted research could easily result in apparent conflicts in conclusions. Those differences are most readily resolved through panel discussions or workshops, which might not occur if different organizations or associations sponsor the different researchers or authors. Some of my work as a trainer came about specifically because I made a comment to the staff of an organization that indexed and made copies of research reports available to the pipeline industry. I pointed out that there were a lot of good related but separate research reports authored about integrity management of vintage pipelines by different research contractors, but no one had developed a summary of the big picture or "what it all means in the end." They agreed it was a good observation and suggested that I do it. A training course that was like a live version of a literature review was born. Key to

its success was links to the various references. In my opinion, many in the industry could benefit by more effort on the part of research leadrs or publishers to collect, summarize, and present highlights of technical advancements covering specific topics instead of each information consumer having to independently collect and review a variety of individual reports or other publications.

Some difficulties in timely implementation occur long before the SME obtains the report. In some models of industry R&D, researchers perform the work and write the draft report which is then reviewed and approved by industry representatives before publication. Peer review by pipeline operator staff plays an important role in ensuring technical accuracy. When reviewers are taken from the population of potential end-users it also helps ensure applicability to real-world situations. The downside of extensive peer review is that the reviewers are usually expected to perform the review function in addition to performing their normal job functions. Generally, (and understandably) company tasks are prioritized more highly than support for publication of industry R&D results. As a result, at times (and in the author's experience) some draft reports have required more than two years to work through the review, revision, and publication process after the report has been submitted by the authors for review. By the time of publication, the work could be superseded by new information that was published in a timelier manner by other sources or in other formats.

Problems with obtaining timely review and consensus in the peer review process has led at least one membership-based R&D organization to consider alternative forms of the review process. For example, in one proposed model, a few recognized SMEs would be contracted and paid to review and comment on draft reports within a predefined timeframe. In another model, the report would be published by default, with edits made only to address those comments received by a rigorously enforced deadline. The disadvantage of the "publish by default at review deadline" approach is that the absence of comments does not guarantee technical accuracy. Except for the effect on project cost, the use of paid reviewers is preferred because it more likely to ensure technical accuracy combined with improved likelihood of publication in a timely manner. Careful selection of paid reviewers would ensure that the reviewers have both the requisite technical competency and the perspective of an end-user.

I believe there is also a challenge for small companies in the effectiveness of information transfer format. Small companies with more limited budgets are the least likely to participate in research JIPs or attend conferences and may not have many SMEs on staff. Yet, their need to stay abreast of the latest technological developments is no less than that of larger operators. For small companies, live or pre-recorded webinars may represent a more cost-effective mode of information transfer compared to attending multi-day symposia or conferences that require extensive travel time and costs, and more time away from regular office duties. Of course, the webinar format limits the amount of potentially valuable networking opportunities that are part of some other formats.

Scope of the problem Part 2: Getting the information to the right people in a usable format

In my secondary role as a technical trainer, it has become apparent that there is often another large component to the scope of the problem; there is sometimes a disconnect between the company SME and the end-users. It has been enlightening to find, for example, that engineering staff of some companies do not know of the existence of PRCI, despite their company being a member. As a result, they are also unaware of the tremendous collection of free technical reports they can access. In other companies, the staff are unsure of who the designated SME is for a specific topic in their company. They may be aware of the applicable company procedure or policy, but not the basis for the content. Has new information been considered and rejected by the SME who authors the procedure, or is the SME unaware of the new information? This can be particularly frustrating when new information becomes available that provides technically defensible options for solving a problem, but the new information does not yet appear to be included in company procedures or standards.

In some cases, the reports contain significant technical developments, but successful application requires correct use of multiple equations. Reports that do not include equations converted to spreadsheet or "app" format are far less likely to be used, or to be used correctly. However, many times the research project deliverables include no form of software tool to facilitate application. A good example is my experience co-authoring ASME CRTD Vol. 91. "Applications Guide for Determining the Yield Strength of In-service Pipe by Hardness Evaluation." The report was designed to describe how hardness testing could be performed in the field on randomly selected pipe samples to calculate a lower bound estimate of yield strength applicable to the pipeline segment over a range of confidence levels. The report contained many equations related to calibration validity, statistical analysis of the pipe hardness data, and to quality assurance of the data. However, the contract for the project did not include provisions for anything other than a report in paper format. The report was 120 pages long. In that format it would never be used by field personnel who made the hardness tests. I later developed spreadsheets that incorporated the equations to facilitate easy use by test technicians along with a greatly condensed "Field Guide" that walked the end-user through the critical steps. Similar limitations have occurred with reports from other organizations that describe solutions to problems like determining the remaining strength of corroded elbows, or determining the axial strain capacity of corroded or flawed girth welds.

Failure to provide the software tools to facilitate easy application of new technical information is a severe limitation that impacts how easily the new information can be applied in the field. The SME should understand the details of the report and related equations, but the end-users mainly need to know what data to collect and how to plug it in to generate a solution.

Are end-users limited in how or when new information is applied?

There can be widely differing approaches to how new information is applied "in the ditch." The approaches are typically influenced by the extent to which new procedures and processes are limited by regulatory considerations, or by the relative authority of headquarters' staff versus operations personnel. Regarding regulatory limitations, a good example comes from 49 CFR Part 192 (applicable to natural gas pipelines). Before December 1999, §192.713 expressly limited the types of repair methods that could be used to repair imperfections on high stress pipe to cylinder replacement or full encirclement, welded sleeves, regardless of whether improvements in technology provided other technically defensible and cost-effective options. With those limitations, new advancements in repair technologies and the understanding of advantages and limitations of different methods had little value to operators who were required to meet Part 192. Then amendment 192-88 in 1999 changed §192.713 to state that imperfections in high stress pipe could be "...Repaired by a method that reliable engineering tests and analyses show can permanently restore the serviceability of the pipe." The change placed the onus on the pipeline operator to evaluate, select, and apply technically defensible repair methods.

Some regulatory limitations continue to lag far behind technical improvements, thus limiting the ability of pipeline operators to apply latest technology that can provide more cost-effective yet safe operation. For example, some sections of API 1104 "Welding of Pipelines and Related Facilities" standard are incorporated by reference (IBR) into 49 CFR Parts 192 and 195. Those both refer specifically to the requirements of the twentieth edition of API 1104. However, that edition was superseded by the 21st edition in September 2013. As of March 2019, the 21st edition still has not been incorporated by reference, despite informal comments from PHMSA staff that the edition is technically superior to the 20th edition. In the meantime, the 22nd edition is nearing completion and publication by the API 1104 committee.

Industry standards can also inadvertently limit application of new technology. It can take a few years for proposed edits that recognize new technologies to successfully pass committee approval processes, particularly when committee members represent competing interests (manufacturers, contractors, and pipeline operators, for example).

Pipeline operators can also end up limiting their options when general statements referencing industry standards are included in O&M Manuals or project specifications. For example, the broad but prescriptive statement "Procedures shall meet the requirements of ASME B31.4." is far more limiting than "Procedures shall meet the requirements of ASME B31.4 with the following exceptions..."

"Procedures shall meet the requirements of ASME B31.4 unless proposed deviations are reviewed and approved by the Project Engineer" is another more flexible alternative. The two alternative statements allow flexibility in the application of new technologies or information for case-specific applications. This of course, assumes that applicable regulations by the jurisdiction allow any deviations from the referenced standard (B31.4 in this example). Similarly, a statement like "The welding and inspection practices shall meet the requirements of API 1104" in an O&M manual is unnecessarily limiting, since only some sections of API 1104 are incorporated by reference in the federal regulations. Yet, in most cases regulators consider the content of a pipeline operator's O&M manual to be as enforceable as industry standards that are IBR.

Summary

In my experience, successful technology transfer hinges upon two critical steps. First, new information must be readily discoverable. The current state of information technology is such that there is no single easy way to learn about all potentially applicable new pipeline technologies by visiting a few websites. Instead, there are many options for learning about new information that can represent improvements in cost effectiveness and efficiency. I would like to see the industry put more effort into periodically collecting and summarizing all the excellent work being presented and published on specific technical issues. A consumer of the new information would then only have to locate the summary instead of locating and digesting all of the many reports being issued by separate researchers. The summaries should be discoverable by web search, rather than require a user to attend a conference or symposium that targets a specific topic.

Secondly, the new information must be presented in a way that allows timely adaption into simple procedures that are readily applied by end-users. The end-users of technical advancements could be pipeline engineers, technicians or field crews. Researchers and other subject matter experts who develop new technologies would do the industry a great service by improving their focus on making sure that the new information is understandable and easily usable by the end-users. That requires that the researcher or author identify who the end-user is and provide them the tools commensurate with their level of technical sophistication to facilitate easier use of their new developments. The tools could be apps, spreadsheets, or training sessions. Until the researchers and authors more effectively convert their new information into useable tools for the end-user, companies will continue to be dependent upon their SMEs (whether in-house or consultants) to not only find the new information, but to translate complex technical information into easy-to-use procedures with well-defined boundary conditions.

With those points in mind I offer the following recommendations for consideration by both researchers, their sponsors or publishers, and the pipeline companies:

1) **Make your new technical information easy to understand by the target audience**. Even if your audience is other subject matter experts, their lives become a lot easier if the information is in a readily usable format that includes tools (spreadsheets, apps, etc.) for easy application.

2) **Pipeline companies need to recognize that the Internet does not eliminate the need for SMEs.** SMEs might be supplemented by technical generalists, but they cannot be replaced. If the operators don't have SMEs on-staff, they become increasingly dependent upon SME consultants. SMEs need to be actively developed over time and recognized for

their technical talents. Elevating their prestige within the organization will make it easier to attract new technical talent.

3) Recognize that merely searching the web via Google will not find all the pertinent information related to potential technical solutions. Answers come from a variety of sources. The Internet is only one source.

4) Consider better review and summary of the disparate new publications and reports so that pipeline operators and other consumers of the technical information can more readily see the "big picture" and state of the art. While some conferences and workshops focus on a narrow subject area that offers a forum for multiple authors to present their work, seldom is they any accompanying effort to distill all the work into concise summaries.

The evolution of in-line inspection (ILI) in North America— could it have been done better?

Geoff Foreman

I'd direct more resources to In Line Inspection R&D, specifically development to enable pipeline operators be better able to prevent pipeline failures.

How did I get here?

While working as an experimental technician at the British Gas Engineering Research Station in Newcastle England, I was sponsored to attend the University of Northumbria, and attained a BEng Degree in Industrial Engineering. I have over 27 years International experience working initially in Europe (UK), South America, US and currently located in Calgary Alberta, Canada.

I have over 40 years ILI experience with British Gas, PII Pipeline Solutions, GE and Baker Hughes a GE company, in the following areas of expertise;

- Experimental Laboratories and Field Technician on prototype ILI (In Line Inspection) tools,
- Design of MFL ILI tools, Data Analysis, Project Management, Technical sales support, Commercial and Regional

Management, Global Growth and Strategy Leader including
Business Development, and finally a Pipeline Industrial
Advocate in the US and Canada. Testifying at the NTSB enquiry
of the San Bruno accident as the ILI SME.

Introduction

In this chapter I explain the origins of In Line Inspection (ILI, or
"smart pigging") and its use in North America, including:

- Assessing the role and effectiveness of ILI in pipeline safety,
- How ILI is used to Identify the presence, location and
  magnitude of flaws in the pipe steel, which could become
  significant to the integrity of the pipeline, and
- Reflecting on how, in hindsight, ILI could have developed in a
  more productive and effective manner.

I like to think of pipelines as being similar to iron bridges. Bridges are essential in moving from point A to point B and are therefore
a critical element of our transportation infrastructure. They are the
product of sound engineering design and construction, and are built
to last beyond their design life (typically, at least 25 years). We need
them every day and tend to take them for granted, unless they fail. Failure of a bridge can lead to death, injury, economic disruption, and, of
course intense scrutiny. All these essential bridges were constructed,
from material that ages and gets weaker over time, either due to fatigue (continual loading) or corrosion. What do we do? We realize very
quickly that replacing all the bridges would cause a major disruption
to transportation and would be an impossible financial burden on the
national economy.

The solution to the bridge infrastructure issue was to introduce a
regime of periodic inspections and repairs to maintain bridge integrity.
As a result, the operating lives of bridges were extended well beyond
their design lives. We know that back in the 1950s we over-engineered

most structures and therefore if we look after them, they will figuratively last indefinitely. We even design and build new bridges with specific inspection and monitoring requirements as part of the integral build.

I believe these points regarding bridges apply equally to pipelines in North America. A huge infrastructure of pipelines was built across the U.S. in the 1950s, as oil and gas became the main sources of energy, replacing wood and coal, as well as the primary feed stock for chemicals production.

So how did pipeline engineers and operators keep these structures working safely? They did the same as their bridge brethren, they used periodic inspection, maintenance and repairs to keep them in a safe operating condition. However, bridges are much more accessible for inspections than pipelines, the vast majority of which are buried.

A scientific solution was required to create a means of inspecting the length of pipelines without disruption to the purpose and operation of the infrastructure. This would require tools (robots) to travel through the pipelines with the product, taking measurements along the entire circumference of the pipeline, without disrupting the delivery of the transported product. The research in this area led to In-Line Inspection (ILI), an ongoing cycle of periodic inspections, engineering assessments and repairs. As depicted in Fig 1, ILI has become a major component of a pipeline operator's Integrity Management Plan (IMP), which is now a regulatory requirement for operating a hazardous liquid or gas pipeline in the U.S.

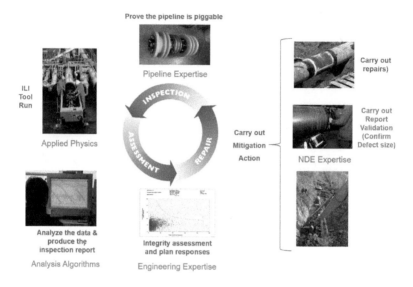

Prove the pipeline is piggable

Pipeline Expertise

ILI Tool Run

INSPECTION

ASSESSMENT

REPAIR

Applied Physics

Carry out repairs)

Carry out Report Validation (Confirm Defect size)

Carry out Mitigation Action

NDE Expertise

Analyze the data & produce the inspection report

Analysis Algorithms

Integrity assessment and plan responses

Engineering Expertise

Figure 1. ILI is a process – not just about technology.

In order to reach its fullest potential in assuring pipeline integrity, ILI needed to overcome several challenges, including;

- Educating the pipeline community in the science of the technologies (e.g., sensors) and their capabilities to assure the correct application of the tools being used in the inspection of the specific types of pipe flaws (e.g., corrosion, cracking, dents and geometry changes).
- Thus, achieving confidence in its use, by creating a proven track record of validation.
- Stimulating competition and cost effectiveness, by creating a competitive, value-added ILI Industry.
- Gaining acceptance and incorporation into Industry standards, codes of practice and regulations. Demonstrating the trust and confidence in ILI to the Industry, regulators and the public.
- Developing, testing, and introducing advances to existing technologies and new innovations including the availability of

test facilities and adequate opportunities to run test tools in operating pipelines.

The origins of ILI tools and their science

ILI tools originated in the U.S. as an extension of oil well services, specifically downhole logging. Down hole logging utilizes robots that are dropped vertically down the well on wires to take measurements along the interior wall of the well. At the inception of pipeline pigging, the only internal pipeline pig passage was done by cleaning devices (rubber spheres) or single body cleaning pigs. These cleaning pigs consisted of hard circular bodies with steel flanges welded to each end as well as rubber or polyurethane cups/discs attached to the flanges to form seals to the pipe wall. The pig body sometimes included brushes and magnets, the former to clean the debris off the pipe wall and the latter to catch construction debris and any ferrous material such as welding rod ends. These were used to clean during the post-construction phase and to enhance the efficiency of liquid throughput or dewatering of gas pipelines during the pipelines' working life.

It became best practice in the United States to test "drill pipe and casing" prior to installation in an oil or gas well. This was achieved by tethering a logging device using magnetic flux leakage (MFL) techniques (see Fig 2 for the physics) The MFL is pulled through the pipe while lying on the ground, using a winch mechanism, thus the origin of the term "pull through." Later, more sophisticated logging devices were developed to measure well pressure and temperatures as well as the casing pipe wall thickness. The tool is inserted into the pipe string at the well head, being dropped vertically inside the installed well casing, usually on a regular basis as a safety procedure. These down hole loggers continue to be developed for more finite and complex flaw discovery and well condition monitoring.

How MagneScan Works -
Detect Magnetic Flux Leakage

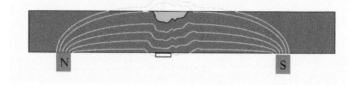

A strong magnetic field must saturate the pipe wall

Lines of magnetic flux will be deflected where:

there is metal loss inside the pipe wall

there is ferrous material near the pipe wall

if the properties of the pipe wall steel change

MFL's primary sensors detect and measure any magnetic flux leakage

Figure 2. How magnetic flux leakage works.

Pigs — what are they?

Over the years, several theories have emerged to describe how ILI tools became known as "pigs." Some claim it's an acronym for Pipeline Inspection Gauge; however, this is not likely as the term "pig" was being used for non-intelligent cleaning tools well before the advent of ILI tools. Others surmise it is due to the sounds – sometimes described as squeals - emanating from these cleaning devices as they travel through a pipeline. However, the most intriguing theory is based upon the method by which the Romans cleaned their drainage pipes. The Romans attached pig bladders to long poles and pushed through the pipes, resulting in the term "pigging the pipe."

Prior to the 1970s, the first intelligent pigs were developed in the form of caliper tools being run to check for geometry changes, dents and buckles in pipelines. These are known as free-swimming tools and they move through the pipe in the pipeline product or compressed air. Unlike the tethered tools, they gather and store data on board, requiring post-pigging data download and analysis. A typical caliper pig is shown in Fig. 3 The silver-colored sensor fingers travel on the inside of the pipe and detect any deformations, while the blue polyurethane cups create a seal with the interior pipe wall. This seal allows the product to drive the pig through the pipeline, similar to a piston in an engine.

Pre-1980's Magnetic Flux Leakage (MFL) tools were adapted into free swimming tools from the tethered logging devices. These devices were fitted with sealing cups and used similar data processing and storage as the caliper tools mentioned earlier. These tools varied in size from as small as 4" dia. up to the 48" dia. tool, an example of which can be seen in Fig. 4.

Figure 3. Typical caliper pig.

Figure 4. Typical MFL tool.

Free swimming capability

Pipelines are built to continuously move large quantities of hydrocarbons to industrial processing and power plants. These plants include refineries and gas processing plants which are responsible for the continuous production of important products such as gasoline, aviation fuel and diesel as wells as many other essentials such as electricity to the grid. How do we inspect these pipelines without disruption to the flow and delivery of products?

One way this key concern was addressed was through the invention and installation of pig traps or pigging stations, Fig. 5. These pigging stations look and operate similar to how a submarine loads and fires torpedoes. It consists of a pressurized door at the end of a piece of pipe that is larger than the pipeline diameter by at least 2-inch. Its connected by a series of valves and interlinking pipework. These installations are tapered to the size of the actual pipeline to be inspected which allows the ILI tool to seal at the front at launch or loose drive as it comes to the end of the pipeline segments, and thus "TRAP" the pig. These stations are connected to the main pipeline at regular intervals, forming pipeline "segments." Many North American pipeline operators had to build or modify existing stations to accommodate the introduction of the "smart pigs," as they were typically longer than the single-module cleaning pigs or spheres being launched and received.

What is required to have a successful ILI tool run?

In order to achieve a successful ILI tool run, the tool must function correctly and collect accurate data along the entire pipeline segment being inspected. To achieve this, the tool must be robust enough and have sufficient power and recording space to inspect a given segment of pipe. The pipeline must also be clean and free of loose debris and paraffin wax, the presence of which could affect the operation of the on-board sensors. The pipeline operations must be continual and constant, within windows of pressure, temperature and flow rate. The ILI tool vendor provides the optimum operating window to the pipeline operator, and the two parties agree on what the inspection operating parameters will be. The flow rate and line segment length are used to calculate the predicted speed of the tool and thus its range. Using the battery life in Amp/hr, and the amount of data which needs to be stored during the ILI tool run, it can be established whether the tool needs to make a single pass or multiple passes (which is done via an on/off delays program on the tool).

Preparations for an ILI inspection depends upon several critical success factors:

- The pipeline operator identifies the length of the pipeline to be inspected (distance between pigging stations), referred to as the inspection segment length (ft).
- The ILI Tool vendor selects the sensor sampling rate along the pipeline, (usually around every 0.1") which allows the calculation of the amount of readings to be processed and stored on the tool.
- The ILI vendor provides the number and capacity of the tools' batteries (Amp/ hrs) to allow the calculation of tool range. As power is time related, it is critical to calculate how long the tool requires power in the pipeline. The ILI vendor will use the product flow rate and length of the pipeline section to estimate this "power on" requirement. The ILI vendors know how much power the tools need to gather and store the data, and can therefore determine if the pipeline will be fully inspected at the pipeline segment specific flow rate. The speed of the product being moved through the pipeline, referred to as the product flow rate (ft/sec). As the tool will travel with the product, it is possible to calculate when the tool will run out of power or fill its recording devices.

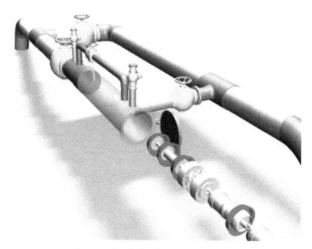

Figure 5. A typical pig launcher.

Magnetic ILI

As ILI was introduced in both Canada the USA, it became apparent that MFL technology could not be a one size fits all application. Occasionally, flaws were discovered after an MFL run to either be larger than predicted or not reported at all. Upon investigation it was apparent that axially aligned flaws, especially narrow slot or groove shaped corrosion was not being seen correctly by MFL. It was being reported as a series of corrosion pits in a line, when in reality it was a single long narrow corrosion feature.

The physics for MFL as shown in Fig. 1 relies on the magnetic flux lines cutting through the flaw ideally at 90 degrees to produce the maximum leakage effect for the sensors to read. It makes it very good at finding and measuring circular pitting and larger general corrosion, both on the inside and outside surface of the pipe (see Fig. 6). However, if the metal loss is axially aligned and narrow (narrow groove shaped corrosion running along the length of the pipe section, typically along the seam weld), MFL cannot size or describe it correctly.

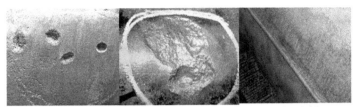

Pitting GeneralNEACC Circumferential Magnetic Field

Figure 6. Types of corrosion metal loss and corresponding magnetic field.

This newly discovered axial flaw was named Narrow Axial External Corrosion (NAEC), and it required a detection approach different than standard MFL. The ILI scientists determined that MFL could work if the magnets were turned through 90 degrees thereby introducing a "circumferential magnetic field." The resultant tool was called the transverse field (TFI) or circumferential magnetic flux leakage (CMFL) ILI tool. This was introduced in 1997 and gained renown as the preferred tool for pipeline long-seam weld inspections (the seam weld joins the rolled metal plate into a circular shape, thus forming the pipes circular shape). The effectiveness of MFL tools depends upon the ability of its sensors to determine the amount of magnetic flux that leaks out of the pipe due to the missing ferrous material resulting from the defect. Fig. (vi) shows the detection of the disturbance caused by axially aligned features is greater with CMFL. Consequently, CMFL is more accurate and reliable for inspecting axially aligned corrosion features, such as NEAC.

Ultrasonic ILI tools

In 1985, TransCanada pipelines, developed an ultrasonic corrosion inspection tool (Fig. 7), in conjunction with the German ILI company,

Pipetronix. This tool uses conventional piezo-electric ultrasound sensors mounted on a flexible polyurethane sensor carrier. The carrier is held on the inside of the pipe by an expanding spring built into the inside of the polyurethane, ensuring continual contact with the pipe wall. These sensors generate a sound wave at a fixed frequency and focus the sound to enter the pipe wall at 90 degrees (perpendicular to the inside pipe wall) and bounce off any surface it passes through, typically the inner and outer surfaces of the pipe itself, and any corrosion or voids in the steel. The sensor measures the time the sound waves take to return to their source, this is called "time of flight" UT inspection. This provides an accurate measurement of the actual pipe wall thickness, and why this sensor array is called a UT wall measurement tool. It also enables the sensor to follow the actual profile of the metal loss, both on the inside and outside surfaces of the pipe. This is particularly important when determining the remaining wall thickness along the length of any corrosion, and is referred to by fracture mechanics Engineers as the "river bottom profile" of the corrosion.

A typical small-diameter ultrasonic wall measurement (USWM) ILI tool is shown in Fig. 7. The sensor carrier is located at the rear of the tool, the other four modules contain the power, electronics and storage units. It is a more accurate means of inspection for corrosion than MFL, but is less robust, requiring the inner pipe surface to be free of any debris that could restrict the sound being returned to the sensors, resulting in "echo loss." It is also speed sensitive, as it needs to catch the returning sound within milli-seconds of being fired, and therefore needs to travel slower than MFL tools, and ideally at a constant speed. Another major factor for using this type of tool is that a liquid medium must be present between the sensors and the internal pipe wall, which allows the transmission of the ultrasound waves. Thus, refined product pipelines are ideal for this type of ILI, consisting of a clean liquid and traveling at a constant velocity. However, with the absence of a liquid medium, the USMW tool is not practical for gas pipeline inspections.

Figure 7. Typical ultrasonic metal loss tool.

ILI Specifications, ASME ANSI B31.G and POF

Although the original analogue MFL tools reported a corrosion feature indicating depth, width and length. As the analysis was manual and carried out immediately after the inspection, ILI vendors would only report the largest metal loss feature in any single joint of pipe (usually 54ft weld to weld). The analysis data was printed onto a "light sensitive rolling plot." This "log" was left with the operator to determine whether other features were contained within the joint. From this further analysis, the operator could determine the kind and number of needed repairs.

The use of the MFL tool resulted in what is described as a "pig and dig" culture, where operators would mobilize an excavator and some pressure containment repair shells to the site, as part of the ILI program. Although this approach enabled a very proactive ILI response that removed the most immediate threats, it was not the most efficient use of resources, considering permitting and onsite costs. If subsequent repairs were required in the same or close-by locations, a longer-term, planned maintenance strategy would be more cost efficient. To achieve this efficiency, the operator needs to be capable of predicting the time smaller flaws will grow to a critical size or coalesce into larger more dangerous features. The "corrosion growth rate" is needed for this next stage, enabling preventative measures being implemented, to either slow down or to remove the corrosion mechanisms. More information was required about the pipeline steels, their corrosion resistance, effectiveness of external coating and cathodic protection methods. (CP is a form of protection by inducing an electric current onto the pipe and some sacrificial material such as zinc. By electrolysis, the lower based material would sacrifice itself and leave the pipe steel intact).

As engineers were researching pipe steels and modes of failure it became very apparent that modern ductile steels could tolerate many smaller flaws without causing any safety risks to the pipeline. The steel strength, remaining wall thickness (under the corrosion), the length of the corrosion and the internal pressure, taken together, can determine whether or not a pipe would contain the pressure, leak or fail catastrophically (rupture). A brain trust of fracture mechanics experts, and pipeline engineers were performing live full-scale testing on these functions and theories, in Europe and in the USA. The result was a pressure-based code of practice, ASME ANSI B31G, published by the American Society of Mechanical Engineers (AMSE). This work produced a curve derived from the pipeline wall thickness, pipe grade and operating pressure. The length and depth of corrosion features are plotted onto the graph and engineers could assess the severity of any individual corrosion feature in a pipeline as to its likelihood of failure (see Fig. 8).

In the late 1980s, early 1990s ILI vendors had the advantages of new smaller and faster digital electronics, replacing the old analogue systems, which greatly changed the amount and rate of data that could be processed and recorded on board the pig. Instead of using multi track tape recorders that were very large, used a lot of power and produced unwanted heat inside the electronics packages, being replaced initially by cassettes and hard drives and ultimately solid- state memory chips. This quickly enabled the amount of data points required for ILI reporting to incorporate these graphs in their inspection results to aid pipeline engineers and technicians in evaluating every feature, and not just one per joint. This new ILI inspection feature in B31 was called "pressure-based reporting" (see Fig. 8). The green indications represent the length and depth of every piece of metal loss contained in the pipeline segment. The curve provides the boundary between pressure containment (below) and potential failure (above). It contains a factor of safety, all the features with red circles have been selected as the most severe using pressure (length and depth), rather than just depth alone. It demonstrates very clearly the fact that long features (or inter-linked connecting corrosion) can fail a pipeline even though they may not be the deepest, compared to shorter features. This proved that the original depth-based ILI reporting was flawed, and that pressure-based reporting was the safest and most realistic means of managing corrosion in pipelines.

Later, some of the conservatism of B31 was removed when the absolute length of a defect was removed in favor of "effective length." Additional research led to a refinement in the length influence enabling the segmenting of a long piece of corrosion into small linear increments. These smaller linear increments further enabled an iterative calculation to produce a predicted burst pressure. This new method of defect evaluation is called RSTRENG. The science behind RSTRENG was developed in the late 1990's and it depicts the remaining strength of a piece of pipe containing a specific corrosion site. RSTRENG was easily adapted for ILI tools as they scan the full circumference of the pipe every 0.1" as they travel along the pipe. So, although individual incremental measurements already existed, the RSTRENG iteration optimized their value to a successful ILI run. In 1994, the Shell Pipeline Company (Holland) formed an Industry Pipeline Operator Forum (POF) for ILI. This work produced a more practical specification for corrosion ILI because it recognized the effects on ILI tools of the different morphologies of flaws. As a result, ILI vendors were induced to provide different tolerances for initially 5 different shapes and orientations of corrosion, and later further refined to seven types (see Fig. 9). One consequence of this work was the introduction of specifications for "pin hole" corrosion, based on the ILI tools now being capable of identifying, and thus discriminating, these features from pitting. In 1998, ILI vendors were improving the resolution of MFL through use of a higher density of smaller sensors. This work also led to a better differentiation between grooving and slotting metal loss. In Fig. 9 the revised POF specification table is depicted with the CMFL tools' capability "sweet spot" highlighted by the dark shading.

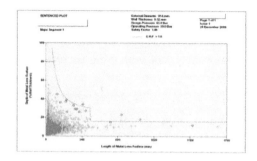

ASME B31.G method

Figure 8. ASME B316 depth versus length plot for metal loss anomalies.

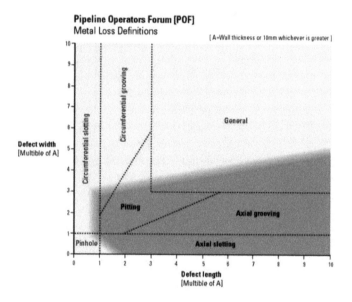

Figure 9. POF depictions of sweet spot for metal loss detection.

Mapping

In the 1980s, the US military were using satellite and robotic technologies in what they described as the new digital warfare era. The Global Positioning System (GPS) was used to target and navigate cruise missiles and smart bombs. This science provided the technology that could be reversed engineered and incorporated onto a pig to determine the global position of pipelines on digital maps. This could then be used in determining whether pipelines were in locations that made them vulnerable to naturally occurring environmental events, such as earthquakes, washouts, floods and landslides.

In 1986 the GEOPIG was launched to map pipeline center lines. This was a massive step forward in the industry for location purposes, enabling trackers and excavators to accurately select sites along a pipeline using transportable GPS equipment, rather than physically measuring along the ground (a process called chaining). Chaining is very time consuming and, more importantly, inaccurate as a component of an ILI run. This inaccuracy is due to the fact that chaining is intended to determine the absolute distance travelled by the pig; however, pipelines follow the contours of the ground, and therefore distances recorded in the vertical plane will cause lateral positioning errors versus the distance travelled along a pipeline right of way.

Over time, GPS satellites became more accessible and the onboard "inertial mapping units" (IMUs) were refined and miniaturized. In addition, portable GPS devices got smaller and more accurate, thereby greatly improving the ability to locate dig sites to within a few feet. ILI tools using IMU's can also provide sufficient information to determine strain on the pipe caused by its movement (See Fig. 10). As the pipeline Industry moved into the world of digital database information technology, for storing and manipulating all pipeline related data, ILI GPS pipeline center lines became critical in aligning all relevant pipeline data with the virtual pipeline on digital maps.

As a consequence, very few ILI runs today do not include onboard GPS in the form of an IMU. Using the digital data base info, GPS also enabled the overlaying of multiple ILI runs and technologies to get a more realistic view on what is happening on any piece of pipeline. Fig. 10 shows the presence of two large deformations or movements in red from the original pipeline position shown in gray, after overlaying two IMU ILI runs.

Figure 10. Graphical display of pipeline movement detected by IMU tool.

Crack detection (CD ILI)

Another threat to pipelines, which magnetic ILI tools struggled to detect and size, is cracking. Axially-oriented cracks can form and grow by fatigue (pressure cycling) or by environmental conditions, combined with stress, thereby creating stress corrosion cracking (SCC). Although ultrasound technology has been successful for many years in detecting and sizing cracks using handheld equipment, the challenge was to incorporate this feature on a pig. MFL tools cannot reliably detect cracks because, by definition, they have no width so there is no magnetic flux leakage to be captured. Similarly, conventional UT sensors were not the answer as they need a coupling between the sensor and the inside of the pipe.

In 1982, British Gas developed a UT Elastic Wave tool with sensors mounted inside an oil-filled wheel for gas pipeline ILI (see Fig. 11). "This was a very problematic tool to run because keeping the oil medium in the wheels without gas ingress inside very high-pressure gas environments was not easy to achieve. It also had feature discrimination issues, in selecting cracks from every other flaw type, such as naturally occurring inclusions and laminations inside the pipe steel. An alternative solution for gas pipelines was required, and in 2002 the first EMAT (Electro Magnetic Acoustic Transducer) pig (see Fig. 12) was introduced in North America to replace the Elastic Wave tool. EMAT does not need a coupling between the sensor and the pipe wall, and therefore became the ideal tool for gas pipeline crack ILI.

Ultrasonic wall measurement pigs had been introduced in 1985 for corrosion in liquid pipelines (see Fig. 7). Adapting and improving this tool to be a crack detection tool was achieved in 1994. Pipeline operators were initially happy to simply find out if and where cracks existed in their pipelines so they could undertake immediate remediation. This ILI was achieved via the ultrasonic crack detection tools (USCD, see Fig. 13). To obtain crack sizing with ILI CD tools originally required calibration, using in-ditch measurements as reference points. External factors such as seasonal weather, permitting, and excavation work meant it could take up to 12 months to get a final CD-sized report from the ILI vendor.

Traditionally, the ILI industry takes its lead from the conventional non-destructive testing (NDT) industry. This was true in the field of Phased Arrays UT which was gaining popularity in the area of crack inspection in the ditch, being seen as an advancement on conventional UT measuring techniques and equipment. Phasing of the ultrasonic beam gives greater adjustment capabilities, refinement and flexibility.

The initial Phased Array ILI tool was introduced in 2004 (see Fig. 14). Full-scale burst testing by research institutes and improved fracture mechanics engineering with crack type defects, resulted in crack assessment methodology being introduced into codes and best practice documents. This prompted the demand on ILI vendors to improve the accuracy of crack dimensions, rather than just crack detection. Pipeline operators and regulators were pushing to reduce the reporting delivery times and to remove the need for post-inspection calibrations of the tool results. Advances in electronics and improved tool resolution, enhanced analysis algorithms, and operator partnering enabled ILI vendors to launch crack absolute depth sizing by 2010. Figs. 11-14 show the various ILI crack sensing and tool types. The technology developed to replace the EW tool, EMAT is also shown, where the need of a liquid coupling is not required. The EMAT sensor rides very close to the pipe wall and an electromagnetic charge produces a sound wave inside the pipe steel. The wave travels around the pipe and is received by an adjacent sensor, or in a case of a crack being present, the wave will return to the transmitting sensor.

The conventional liquid USCD tool is shown at a launch site and the Phased Array ILI tool shows how the sensor carrier's arrays are very different from the USCD tool.

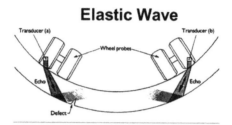

2 MHZ 65° SHEAR WAVE (SV) DETECTS CRACKS & THEIR CIRCUMFERENTIAL POSITION

TRANSMITTED WAVE CONTROLS TOOL CALIBRATION

Figure 11. Elastic Wave sensors.

Figure 12. EMAT sensor and Carrier

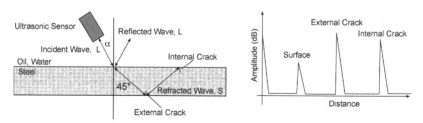

Figure 13. USCD sensor carrier (left) and firing mechanism (right).

Figure 14. Phased Array sensor and carrier.

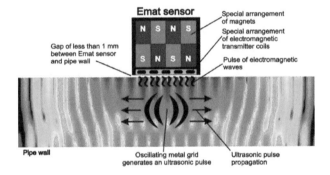

Figure 15. EMAT sensor and carrier.

Figure 15. EMAT sensor and carrier.

Mechanical damage

Statistics show that the biggest threat to pipelines comes from mechanical damage. Pipelines can be dented or gouged by third party construction machinery such as the teeth of diggers or trenchers. Because pipelines are filled with high pressure gas or liquids, they can deform from the initial impact and then later re-round due to the internal pressure. Once the pipe steel has yielded to deform, it will affect its strength properties. It is therefore important to identify any signs of impact especially on the top and sides of the pipe.

Some dents contain metal loss and cracking due to the gouging action of the digger teeth. These are very dangerous flaws that need to be addressed quickly. Caliper ILI tools can identify dents and buckles but cannot determine if they contain metal loss or cracking. A combination of ILI technologies needs to be run and overlaid to make that distinction. Combo or combination MFL, Caliper and IMU are run as one tool and can determine the existence of a dent, whether it has any metal loss associated with it, and whether the force causing it has moved the pipeline. The Caliper will indicate the dent, the MFL will identify any metal loss within the dent area and the IMU will indicate if the pipeline center line has changed. To identify cracking inside a dent, a crack detection (CD) tool must be run and the ILI data overlaid onto the caliper/ IMU data.

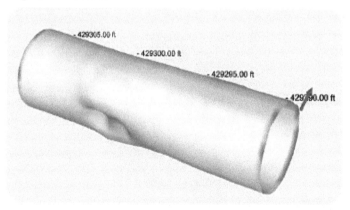

Figure 16. A severely dented pipe.

Figure 17. ILI MFL Caliper combo tool.

Confidence in the use of ILI - creating a good track record for validation

Having committed to running new technology ILI tools in a pipe-line, it is necessary to establish a validation program that includes as many tool-testing and proving runs as practicable. Both the ILI vendor and the operator need to agree what determines the "success" or "fail" criteria of a test run and how many successful inspections are required to confirm validation. Most important to the ILI vendors is the num-ber of digs the operator is prepared to conduct on "non-safety sized" defects. These are smaller defects than would require remediation and are essential to fine tuning the sizing algorithms. In a regulated indus-try such as in the USA, the pipeline regulator, PHMSA, needs to also agree with the criteria established for success and be prepared to allow all operators to use the technology and abide by its results. ILI ven-dors are not regulated by PHMSA, so the onus falls on the operators to lead the acceptance of the results with the agency. In some instances, a number of operators have formed joint industry projects (JIP) and included briefings with PHMSA and state regulators, thereby sharing the test run program among all key stakeholders. Some operators have been unwilling to work with the ILI vendors and regulators because of potential legal issues that might arise. These operators fear that some new pipeline problems will be revealed that were not envisaged, during the development of a specific ILI technology.

Competition and cost-effectiveness of ILI in the US — creating a competitive, value-added tool for the pipeline industry

Most operators in the USA want open competition between the ILI vendors to stimulate quality improvements and to put competitive pressure on pricing. Some operators will openly encourage, partner with, or sponsor an ILI vendor who doesn't possess a particular technology or process. In so doing, operators seek to prevent creation of a monopoly by any one ILI vendor, and thereby create a level playing field when bidding for ILI contracts. In the past, the cost and resources needed to invent, design, build and test ILI tools were prohibitive and a real barrier to entry for newcomers in the Industry. This is no longer the case for Caliper and MFL tools, whose components and software are proprietary and available at reasonable prices. Also, many of the ILI vendor technology personnel have moved around the industry so that intellectual property (e.g., patents) interests have been diluted and present no real impediments to new entrants. Also, the age of the ILI industry is such that most conceptual patents have expired. The newer technologies such as CD and EMAT are still protected by patents and their component and testing costs are much higher than caliper and MFL. Thus, only a few ILI vendors offer CD services today. However, just as with MFL/Calipers, this will no doubt change over time as crack tool components and knowhow become easier to come by.

DA (Direct Assessment)

ILI in general is a very cost-effective means of inspecting an entire pipeline for all the known and established threats. It has to be used correctly and incorporated with other tools in the operator's IMP. The alternatives to ILI are hydrostatic testing (hydrotesting) and, more recently, direct assessment (DA). DA is utilized on pipelines that are difficult or impossible to pig due to their physical or operational features and limitations. As a statistical estimation of what might be present and where on the pipeline, DA represents a "best engineering available" solution, but it lacks the comprehensive coverage provided by ILI. In addition, it can result in very costly and extensive excavation programs and provides less overall risk coverage.

Hydrostatic testing (hydrotesting)

Hydrotesting can only determine if a significant flaw exists on the day of the testing. Consequently, many unknown latent flaws may exist and go undetected because they are not as significant as the one that fails. Hydrotesting can result in multiple repairs and re-testing over and over until the pipe finally passes a test. Another drawback of hydrotesting is the fact that it requires the pipeline to be taken out of service in order to fill it with test water. Similarly, the water itself poses its own problems, due to the amount required (which may involve multiple test locations), the means necessary to store and dispose of the contaminated water after testing, and the environmental impact of that disposal. Also, the topography of the ROW, especially in mountainous areas, can make hydrotesting almost impossible. This is because typically only very short lengths of pipeline can be tested at any one time due to the hydraulic effect of the different heights along a route.

As hydrotesting requires elevated pressures to be exerted on the pipe steel, it has been proven from experience that it can cause more issues to the integrity of the pipe than benefits. It can grow existing cracks, or cause new ones resulting in what is known as "pressure reversals." Pressure reversals occur after a repair is made based on the result of a hydrotest and a retest is conducted. Upon the post-repair test, the pipeline fails at a pressure lower than the previous test. This can be repeated several times, because the test is growing flaws to significant sizes which fail at pressures lower than those of the previous tests.

The costs of a pipeline failure in terms of both financial and public relations are huge and seriously impact insurance rates and the cost of operating a pipeline in general. In comparison, a good IMP containing the correct use of ILI technologies and vendors with reliable track records is very cost effective and provides real value to the operator.

Acceptance and incorporation into industry standards, codes of practice and regulations — achieving trust and confidence in ILI

One proven means for getting PHMSA buy-in and eventual industry acceptance is to have PHMSA provide research funding for ILI-based solutions. Once the research demonstrates the technical and operational viability of the solution, the next step is to have the solution adopted in the governing regulations. However, to get to that place, the solutions should be written into codes and best practices by industry bodies such as ASME, API, INGAA and NACE. PHMSA has established a protocol of using a selection of these codes and practices for eventual incorporation in regulations. In so doing, PHMSA affirms that they embrace the industry's tried and tested best practices as being a critical component in keeping the pipelines in the US safe. Therefore, the best means of getting a new or improved ILI technology into the regulations is to make sure it is written into these codes and practices, which are usually revised on a five-year basis. If a breakthrough ILI technology or process is developed, and it is essential to apply it immediately without waiting for a revision to be made to the regulations, the operators need to go to PHMSA and get a waiver or an exemption to incorporate the technology or process into their IMPs.

ILI improvements and developments

As indicated previously, improvements, refinements and new technologies have been introduced continuously into the ILI portfolio. The ILI vendors will continue to develop next-generation ILI tools by: incorporating new sensor technologies, with higher definition or resolution; increasing the density of sensors; and, improving range and speeds. This ongoing development usually entails design, build, and test sequences at each vendor's own research centers and are typically veiled in secrecy, to protect their competitive edge.

However, it doesn't matter how many test rigs and simulations are carried out, the real test is when the tool is run in a live pipeline. This typically involves one of two scenarios: 1) an operator allows live testing by an ILI vendor in one of its pipelines; or, 2) two or more operators partner to both develop the technology and make more pipelines available for test runs, after all the simulations and pull testing have been done. In each of these scenarios, the pipelines used for testing need to contain a statistically significant sample of the target flaws, to be able to evaluate tool performance and validate that the new tool's technology actually works. This requires either specially prepared test joints or short pups to be machined and placed into the line for the test runs, or artificial defects being put into selected sections. Validation is always the most difficult part of any new tool development or technology advancement in ILI, and it must comport with the ILI standard in ASME ANSE 1163 regarding the probability of detection (POD), the probability of identification (POI), and the sizing capability of the new tool. This also contributes directly to creation of the actual performance specification based upon the full-scale testing.

Fig. 18 gives a graphic timeline of the historical development of ILI over the 40-year period. The purple arrow representing the magnetic ILI tool technology advances and the green the ultrasonic.

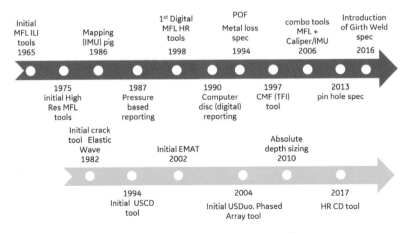

Figure 18. A timeline of the historical development of ILI.

Summary

A combination of advances in electronic components, computing and recording technologies has enabled a rapid development of ILI in the four decades since its inception. In this time, ILI tools evolved from flaw indicators, to integral reliable measuring devices, allowing management and monitoring of flaws. Modern ILI tools prevent immediate costly excavations, most notably on flaws that were not presenting immediate threats to the pipeline. The introduction and development history of ILI in the US is shown in Fig. 17, with the purple arrow indicating the metal loss and geometry tool history and the green representing that of crack inspection.

The biggest challenge for any ILI introduction is getting the funding and resources required to develop these tools in a timely manner. Traditionally, ILI vendors use their own funding and engineering resources to develop new technologies and processes. However, as the competitive landscape has changed over time with many more entrants to the market, causing price reductions and reduced profit margins, thus R&D spending has been impacted. Partnering with some pipeline operators to develop tools for their particular flaws problem has worked, providing the ILI vendors with a guaranteed payback market at the end of the development process, or receiving seed money to cover the development costs from the operators.

Joint Industry projects have also proved very effective on the EMAT development for example, where the majority of US and Canadian gas transmission companies formed an EMAT Users Group to share the onus of validation and providing a larger pipeline pool, to test and prove out the technology.

Then there are the regulations which can dampen the willingness of operators to pioneer new technologies (unless as part of a JIP), due to being exposed individually to regulator or legal scrutiny through public groups and the press. Pipeline companies also need to protect their commercial image and their shareholders. The open reporting of an operator taking part in an ILI tool development program can create the perception they have a major problem with their pipelines, in an environment where the focus is on pipeline failures and anti-pipeline propaganda.

How could it have been done better?

A more open culture when it comes to finding solutions to newly discovered problems, such as new types of flaws that current ILI technology cannot consistently detect. A means where operators, ILI vendors, R&D organizations and regulators can work together in a non-threatening legal and competitive environment. This would speed up both tool development and testing, as well as regulatory acceptance, without potential penalties, such as unrealistic and impractical remedial demands once a solution is found. This would also apply to the ILI vendors as well as the operators, in that a complete fleet of tools (in all size ranges) needs to be designed, built and tested, to cover inspections across an entire infrastructure. This could take years to complete and forcing pipelines to be taken out of service or pressure de-rated until a solution is ready, could paralyze the industry.

Apart from funding there is the acceptance by the pipeline industry. The formation of an industry R&D body such as PRCI, specifically for ILI tool development, would be beneficial. The membership of these bodies would consist of pipeline subject matter experts (SME's) within the operator companies, ILI Vendors and Regulators. By including the regulators would prevent having to educate them after new developments have been achieved. I strongly believe that collaboration between ILI vendors, research and development centers (such as PRCI), operators and regulators could have facilitated acceptance and trust in ILI much more quickly than it did. The US lost a very valuable asset when the Gas Research Institute (GRI) closed its live gas flow test facility. In the early days of Elastic Wave, GRI was instrumental in establishing the capability to find cracks, thereby stimulating a JIP of operators from both the U.S. and Canada to get behind crack detection ILI tools. The ability to collectively carry out live testing for ILI vendors, operators and regulators is priceless. A lot of time could have been saved if that facility existed today in the development of EMAT tools.

The other advantage is that all types of defects can be introduced with known dimensions to test against. If development can only be provided in live pipelines, introducing the target flaws and measuring their dimensions is very expensive to the operators, and is introducing flaws that need to be removed post testing. This causes interruption of the normal operation of the pipeline, in that pressure reductions may have to be applied as "on the pipe" measurements are taken. Typically, a larger scale of excavation is required to prove out the sizing, POD and POI. Excavating entire target pipe and adjacent joints (typically over 100 ft) to see if the tool missed anything, as well as proving out what it did call. These excavations are funded by the operators and therefore seen as a substantial extra expense to normal operations.

PRCI recently built an ILI pull-through facility and a small liquid flow loop in Houston Texas, which will provide a possible alternative facility to test and develop more ILI technologies. However, the ability to test tools in live high-pressure gas and liquids in real life situations is invaluable and still does not exist today. A government funded facility, available to PHMSA and the pipeline industry for research and testing, would be very beneficial for the US Such a facility would focus not only on ILI, but on all operating aspects, including for example, flow metering, leak detection and repair methods.

Joint Industry projects have also proved very effective on the EMAT development for example, where the majority of US and Canadian gas transmission companies formed an EMAT Users Group to share the costs and providing pipelines to test and prove out the technology. Perhaps this is a good financial model for the future and would be even more attractive if government incentives were provided to encourage these companies to partake in such schemes, in the form of tax breaks, or higher tariffs for pipelines that were used in these types of projects.

In considering the future state of ILI technology and capabilities, certain key needs emerge, including, the need for -

A cost-viable program that operators can deploy for pipeline remediation to confront emerging problems, without compromising the ability to generate income or public safety. This needs a safe legal framework that facilitates research projects to be undertaken in the

U.S. where the operators' legal departments don't feel they are exposing their organizations to any legal risk by their participation. Finally, the history of ILI development in the US – the successes and the failures – suggests that perhaps the key success factor going forward is the need for improved dig verification. This element of ILI development demonstrates that had pipeline operators and ILI vendors worked more collaboratively both the pace and capability of ILI technology would have come to fruition sooner.

Consider the following:

Pipeline operators have not been great in the past at sharing all the information they have at their disposal. This often results in the operators having all the proof data of the actual performance of a specific ILI tool, and the ILI vendors being left wondering how well they did. Also, a common trend is for operators to give feedback to the ILI vendors after all the digs have been completed, thus not allowing the ILI vendor concurrent access to the actual flaw being inspected. An operator complaining to the ILI vendor after a dig that the tool has not met the operator's specification, gives the ILI vendor only negative feedback, which in turn can lead the ILI vendor to withdraw an otherwise worthwhile technology under the impression it is not meeting specifications on a regular basis. Worse still is when the operator gives no feedback to the ILI vendor, but rather takes it upon itself to bias or correct, the ILI results based upon their own findings. It is imperative the ILI vendor understands and knows if its tool has over or under-performed to its current operating specification. Reliable data such as sizing trends, are required by the ILI vendor for continuously improvement of the tool's sizing algorithms. Also, flaw identification for better POI analysis. Different flaw types and their morphology will cause different ILI result for specific technologies, and a "one adjustment factor fits all" approach is never a good practice.

In light of the above, and in recognition of the growing regulatory oversight of the U.S. pipeline industry and the increase in the number of ILI vendors operating here, perhaps the future of ILI development will include the ILI industry coming under a regulation. As operators rely on the ILI vendors specification and published track records, it is difficult to differentiate between ILI vendors performance capabilities and selection is usually driven by price. In order to maintain pipeline safety and a PHMSA target of zero pipeline failures, it would benefit everyone if a standard of performance was established, or "you get what it says on the can" report, that can be trusted. Under such a regime, the regulator, either on its own or in collaboration with third parties, would have a test facility that contains a flow loop to run live tools with the ability to swap out various types of defects in test joints. If the ILI vendor correctly located and sized the target defects to their own specification it would become certified to work in the U.S. for the specific flaw types in the test. Conversely, if a vendor failed to perform consistently against its approved capabilities, it would run the risk of the regulator revoking or suspending its US operating license. This would either remove an underperforming ILI service provider from the scene or induce it to revise its capabilities and practices to assure the required standard of performance and quality in their specification was being consistently delivered.

Pipeline integrity management — is the current process flawed?

Dr. Brian N Leis

BY GOD, IF I WERE IN CHARGE…

1. Capture the value of technology and information developed in the 'early years', and minimize duplicative effort unless it clearly leads to a step gain;

2. Better integrate inspection and integrity assessment technologies;

3. Redefine the metrics used to prioritize technology 'needs' and to assess 'value.'

How did I get involved?

I have participated in technology development and its practical applications for decades. The first 39 years were with Battelle Memorial Institute, working at their Columbus Laboratory, when upon retirement I held their title akin to Institute Scientist. At Battelle I worked on integrity assessment and management of transportation and energy systems – with involvement over time ranging from aerospace (space shuttle issues) to buried infrastructure (pipelines). I have since 'retired' to the comfortable working space of my consultancy.

What follows reflects my training in Structural Engineering leading to a PhD (U of Waterloo, Canada), a brief stint teaching (Materials Science / adjunct at Ohio State University), and my work experience in technology development and its practical use – here with a focus on pipelines. I consider integrity management prior to the convergence of inspection and assessment technologies circa 2000, and since. I critique aspects of assessment technology and consider the interface between inspection and assessment as background to establishing the need for change regarding integrity and inspection, and technology success metrics. Given my science background, what follows includes citations that provide historical perspective and/or serve to establish the need for change.

Introduction

In this Chapter I consider transmission pipeline integrity management (IM) focusing on the inspection-based condition assessment approach that took hold circa 2000. The convergence of inspection and assessment technologies is reviewed as the foundation for inspection-based assessment. I then consider inspection-based IM in reference to a few high-profile failures that occurred on recently inspected pipelines, which had been managed using this inspection-based approach. Next, I trend incident statistics as the basis to quantitatively track the effects of changes directed at safety improvements before and since this IM approach was implemented.

In spite of significantly increased investments made to inspect, assess, rehab, and repair such systems, it becomes apparent from the trending that inspection-based assessment has resulted in diminishing returns. Inspection practices that today are directed at managing the larger features are considered in contrast to the loadings and the line pipe properties that resist those loadings, which indicates that the largest features do not always control failure. This, coupled with the diminishing returns from IM investments, suggests that the current IM process is flawed. Finally, I consider whether this IM process is flawed, and thereafter broadly consider causes for the diminishing returns, which points to issues in the inspection and assessment technologies and the interface between them, and in the technology development and management processes.

The convergence of inspection and assessment technologies[*]

Woodley, recently a technical adviser to Pigging Products and Services Association[†], indicated that the first 'intelligent' pig was a caliper tool introduced by TD Williamson (TDW) in 1959 with the purpose of detecting dents.[1] That first-generation technology spawned what today can be considered five generations of caliper / deformation tools, which now can accurately quantify pipeline shape with high precision[2]. Woodley also discussed the development of 'in-line' inspection (ILI) tools that sought to detect metal-loss features via magnetic flux leakage (MFL). He alluded to LINALOG 90°, which debuted circa 1965 and was aptly named because it only inspected the lower 90° of the pipe, and LINALOG 360°, which debuted the following year. Perhaps the first high-value commercial use of this metal-loss technology followed in 1968, as noted in testimony to the NTSB[3] that cited its use regarding the condition of a pipeline in a river crossing. Woodley notes that by the late 1970s the first digital data capacity was coming into play, which would provide the storage necessary if the resolution of such tools was to increase. Given that the early focus was detection, as becomes apparent in later discussion, sizing via MFL was rudimentary well into the 1980s. This in part is due to the initial focus on detection, and the observation that what was designed to detect might in concept or technology not be optimal when adapted for the dual purposes of detection and sizing.

John Grover, a former general manager with GE Oil and Gas, also has provided perspective on the use of nondestructive characterization for that entity's role in developing ILI tools.[4] One key observation was that data capacity needed to increase resolution stretched what could be done using the analog recording schemes then in use. Another key

---

[*] This brief overview borrows heavily from Reference 2, which recently considered such tools and technologies in the context of inspection-based assessment involving mechanical damage. Readers interested in the historical and other details related to these tools and technologies should review that document and its citations.

[†] www.ppsa-online.com

observation was that many cycles of refine and redevelop have continued since in regard to MFL, which is the case for all such sensor
technologies. Developments have occurred in regard to the sensor plat-
forms that permit speed control and afford other benefits. Likewise, the
types of features that can be detected reliably and sized has expanded,
as has the range of pipe sizes that can be so managed.

The initial convergence of inspection and condition assessment
technologies capitalized on the early Level 1[*] assessment methods,
such as B31G[6] and Modified B31G[7], as well as on Level 2 methods such
as RSTRENG[8]. These methods dealt with metal-loss and other blunt
features that failed by plastic (net-section) collapse. These early methods were subsequently augmented by technology such as PCORR/
PCORRC[9], LPC-1[10], and CorLAS[11], which were developed to manage
metal-loss in pipelines made of the higher-strength line-pipe Grades.
Early technology was also available to assess sharp crack-like features
whose failure was controlled by fracture.[12] And as had occurred for
the early collapse-based criteria, this early fracture-based technology
has been updated in the form of Level 2 criteria, like the ductile-flaw-
growth model (DFGM)[13] and a related early-release software package
known as the pipeline axial-flaw failure criterion (PAFFC)[14]. CorLAS[11]
noted above for metal-loss also can be used to assess cracking.

Thus, by the turn of the new millennium the stage was set for the
practical convergence of inspection and assessment, and the analysis
of feature severity in terms of criteria developed to assess both collapse
and fracture-controlled failure. Unfortunately, because this convergence involved technologies that had developed independently over
many decades, the output from the inspection was not always a great
fit with the needs of the assessment. I will pursue this aspect later in
some detail, as it continues to be prevalent.

---

[*] American Petroleum Institute (API) Recommended Practice (RP) 579[5] titled Fitness-for-Service
(FFS) identifies three levels of FFS criteria that reflect increasing technology complexity. Level 1
comprises simple equations, whereas Level 3 comprises the most complex methods, as for
example finite element analysis (FEA). Methods that can be simply packaged as user-friendly
software fall into Level 2.

The new millennium and the decade following

Circa 2000, both the oil and gas (O&G) industry and the Regulators had recognized the benefits that could accrue to inspection-based condition monitoring and integrity assessment. As this activity was then largely focused on the pipeline systems that operated in the United States, the convergence of inspection and assessment will be considered in that framework.

O&G industry developments circa 2000

The O&G Industry was very active in the years leading up to and after the new millennium. The concept that became known as alternative integrity verification (AIV), developed under funding from the Pipeline Research Council International (PRCI), relied on inspection-based condition assessment. This development was reported in considerable detail in 1997[15], and in summary format in 2000[16]. AIV as initially developed was specific to aspects of offshore pipelines, and included consideration of inspection and assessment capabilities, and specifications, with a view to manage the uncertainties in that application.

The 2000 revision of DNV-OS-F101[17] titled Submarine Pipeline Systems was the first codified IM framework to accept the AIV inspection-based assessment approach. That same year fitness-for-service technology became broadly available under the auspices of the American Petroleum Institute (API), in RP 579[5]. Peer-review drafts of the API Standard 1160[18] *Managing Pipeline System Integrity* appeared in September 2000. It incorporated inspection-based condition assessment as an alternative to pressure-proof testing. Drafts of what became a supplement to the American Society of Mechanical Engineers (ASME) Code B31.8 likewise were being developed circa 2000. This supplement, known as ASME 31.8S[19] *Managing System Integrity of Gas Pipelines*, included an inspection-based IM approach for pipelines.

Regulatory developments and pending mandates circa 2000

The years just prior to the turn of the new millennium, and shortly thereafter, also were a period of development and change for the US pipeline Regulatory framework. Development and related change began in the mid-1990s, in response to the Accountable Pipeline Safety and Partnership Act of 1996[20]. A key element of that Act required the Office of Pipeline Safety (OPS[*]) to conduct a Pipeline Risk Management Demonstration Program, whose purpose was to test whether the principles and processes of risk management could provide effective alternative regulatory approaches for the pipeline industry. Accordingly, the OPS sponsored work in conjunction with several Industry Associations. A natural gas pipeline risk assessment quality team (RAQT) was cosponsored by the Interstate Natural Gas Association (INGAA), the American Gas Association (AGA), and the Gas Research Institute (GRI)[+]. The hazardous liquid RAQT was cosponsored by the API. Details of the methodology were published, and related demonstration programs were implemented. (e.g.,21) While the use of such methods is now permitted in the US, they have not been as broadly adopted nor codified to the extent that has occurred in some other codified frameworks, and adopted by some Regulators (e.g.,22).

In parallel with these IM developments, the OPS was drafting notices of pending rulemakings (NOPRs), and subsequently presented final versions of these rules. The NOPRs that first appeared for hazardous liquid systems[23] were followed by those for natural gas systems[24]. Kelley Coyner, then leading the Research and Special Programs Administration (RSPA4), noted in a press conference in early April of 2000 that changes were coming from a Regulatory perspective.[25] Foreshadowing what was to come, she stated "this summer we will see a major overhaul of our safety standards."

---

[*] OPS is housed in the US of the US Department of Transportation under the Pipeline and Hazardous Materials Safety Administration (PHMSA). The RSPA previously held the role that is managed today by the PHMSA.

[+] GRI has since been subsumed by the Gas Technology Institute.

Circa 2000 the US General Accounting Office (GAO) reported that pipeline safety was changing in reference to how the OPS oversees the pipeline industry.[26] About the same time, the US Office of the Inspector General[27] (OIG) stated that the OPS must expand their research and development activities to improve the capabilities of tools referred to as 'smart pigs.' The OIG's comments specifically noted applications involving cracks and select other features, including defects in seam welds.

Impact of the incident near carmichael MS and the NTSB's recommendations

The need to improve inspection capabilities noted by the OIG in 2000 was reinforced when a major incident occurred on a line that a few years earlier was inspected to establish the pipeline's integrity in the framework of inspection-based IM. A rupture occurred near Carmichael MS in 2007 in a segment of a propane pipeline that was constructed using pre-1970 electric-resistance welded (ERW) pipe. The release ignited, causing two deaths and minor injuries to seven others. As well, four houses were destroyed and others damaged.

The NTSB reported[28,29] the probable cause as the failure of a weld. Figure 17[29] and other images in their reports indicate this occurred within the girth-weld upstream of the joint that originated this failure. They added[28] that this weld failure "caused the pipe to fracture along the longitudinal seam weld... and portions of the adjacent pipe joints." Others also have considered the circumstances of this incident, and report (e.g., 30) in direct conflict with the NTSB that the likely cause of the seam-split lay within axial ERW seam anomalies that were clearly evident in NTSB images that were captured within the length of this seam split. Key in support for this conflicting failure sequence was the observation that Chevron's on-the-split seam, located within inches of the upstream girth-weld, pointed away from that girth-weld – back to an origin along the longitudinal (long) seam – in direct conflict with the NTSB's reported sequence.

Because the IM Plan for this pipeline was among those implemented shortly after condition-based IM was implemented the question could be asked – was this IM approach contributory to this failure? The pipeline had been inspected just two years prior using a then current-generation crack tool. While two long-seam anomalies were reported in the joint that originated the rupture, it was later stated that they did not then meet the criteria for reportable indications[31]. Sizing uncertainty thus became a potential contributing cause, and perhaps led the NTSB to conclude in 2009 that the "current inspection and testing programs are not sufficiently reliable to identify features associated with longitudinal seam failures of ERW pipe prior to catastrophic failure." Unfortunately, the recommendations made by the NTSB[31] in many ways echoed the words of the US OIG[27] almost a decade prior in regard to the limitations of crack tools.

With a view to improving the viability of inspection-based condition assessment and to address the NTSB's recommendations, the Pipeline and Hazardous Materials Safety Administration funded a major study directed at actions to eliminate catastrophic failures in ERW seams and assess the effectiveness of key elements of inspection-based IM. But, in view of the published outcomes of that two-phase, multi-year project[33,34], I contend that gaps remained in their reporting and that work remains before AIV might be relied on broadly as the sole basis for IM. In this context it is instructive to consider other inspect-then-fail scenarios for incidents where the ILI technology was matched to the reported cause of the failure.

Overview of some Inspect-then-Fail scenarios

Pipeline accidents have been tabulated for the US[35], with some parsed by year[36] and others parsed by century[37]. Although the information is available, little has been done to assess the viability of ILI as a function of the type of tool and/or anomaly, or to track the effects of the evolution of ILI technology. The outcomes of the work directed by PHMSA subsequent to the Carmichael incident also considered the viability of ILI(38,39), but the databases developed were limited.

To broaden the outcomes of that work, the results of failure analysis and inspection details, either available by experience or openly from PHMSA[*] or the NTSB[†], have been reviewed to identify cases where a pipeline was inspected and then failed prior to its next planned or mandated revalidation and/or related inspection.[‡] While a comprehensive review would be instructive here, it will suffice to reflect on several high-profile events to identify and illustrate some trends. (The downside of this approach focused on failures is that nothing is learned about when and why such inspections are viable.)

Observations concerning Inspect-then-Fail scenarios

Review of many inspect-then-fail scenarios leads to the following broad observations:

1. Occasionally the design and/or operation of a pipeline does not facilitate the type of inspection that is necessary to ensure its continued safe operation;

2. Occasionally more was anticipated or expected from an ILI tool and the resulting inspection than has been possible for a given type of feature or technology;

3. Occasionally tools don't detect an anomaly of the type they are designed to find and size, or they misidentify or incorrectly size it even though the feature exceeds their specified thresholds – likewise the inspection data logs are misread or misinterpreted by an expert analyst or by the Vendor's algorithms – with this uncertainty evident in the low-resolution metal-loss caveat "accurate within ±10%, with 80% confidence";

4. Threats to pipeline integrity were active but occasionally unrecognized, or were active at a growth rate beyond that antici-

---

[*] PHMSA: https://www.phmsa.dot.gov/safety-reports/pipeline-failure-investigation-reports
[†] NTSB: https://www.ntsb.gov/investigations/accidentreports/pages/pipeline.aspx
[‡] Part 195 of Title 49 of the US Code of Federal Regulations (CFRs) deals with HL pipelines and terms unplanned releases 'accidents'. CFR Part 192 that deals with NG Systems uses the term accident in cases of overpressure, but refers to unplanned events like releases as 'incidents'. This notation is used hereafter, with the term incident used in generic discussion.

pated, such that absent the recognized need an inspection was not scheduled, and/or the revalidation interval was too long.

The first of these observations reflects hard-to-inspect scenarios, such as stub or low-flow / low-pressure pipe segments, or design aspects like crossovers. As such, the available inspection data are limited, such that anomalies that have caused accidents cannot be contrasted to physical evidence to illustrate what experience has shown. In contrast, the last three observations can be broadly illustrated, as follows.

Select illustrations of Inspect-Then-Fail incidents

Perhaps the first inspect-then-fail occurrence involved the 1994 Edison, NJ rupture[40], which preceded the shift to condition-based IM. Aspects of this incident were reconsidered by the NTSB leading to revision of their report[41]. That revised reporting included the possibility that the causative feature for this incident was present at the time of a metal-loss in-line inspection done eight years prior. Although uncertainty exists in the details, this incident is considered because it clearly illustrates most aspects of observation #2 above. For example, dialog in this reporting makes it clear that occasionally tools don't detect an anomaly of the type they are designed to detect and size. It shows that "smart pigs" do misidentify or incorrectly size, even though the feature exceeds their specified thresholds. Finally, this incident reporting illustrates that inspection data logs can be misread, or misinterpreted, even by experts. Such continues to be the case, which is again evident in regard to the 2015 oil spill off the coast of Santa Barbara[42]. The capabilities of inspection tools are expressed in terms of probability of detection, with outcomes described above: are the current in-line tool specifications adequate?

Other inspect-then-fail incidents shortly after the transition to inspection-based IM involved a) the rupture of a gasoline pipeline and subsequent fire[43] and b) the release of fuel oil from the Piney Point Pipeline[44]. The NTSB report for the first incident makes clear the uncertainty involved in interpreting inspection logs circa the 1990s. The second illustrates cases where uncertainty concerning the feature(s) involved opens to the chance that more is anticipated or expected from a tool and the resulting inspection than is possible for a given combination of ILI tool and feature type. This concern remains today. A more recent incident involving a leak through a shallow dent that initiated cracking due to fatigue[45] serves to illustrate observation #4.

Figure 1 shows the failure through the Piney Point Pipeline. Figure 1a shows the failure after the line was exposed and the coating removed, while Figure 1b shows the still coated pipeline as excavated, such that the cracking is hidden. While the image in Figure 1b is reminiscent of a wrinkle bend, this pipeline was constructed decades after this practice was abandoned, and so must be a buckle formed due to outside forces.

The November 1995 ILI included a geometry tool run and a MFL tool run, but as reported by the NTSB[44] the ILI Report identified this feature as a Tee, so it was considered no further. Personal experience with some deformation / geometry tools indicates that they have greatly improved since, so that with the choice of the correct tool this feature would not be misidentified as a fitting.

Many illustrations of failures following inspections – like that for the Carmichael incident – can be identified in the archives of the NTSB and the PHMSA that are consistent with the limited ILI effectiveness as reported by Kiefner et al circa 2013[38]. While results for more recent tools and new tool concepts painted a more positive picture (e.g.,39), recent catastrophic incidents like that at Santa Barbara[42] suggest that the industry still has a way to go before inspection-based condition assessment and IM can even approach INGAA's stated goal[47] of 'zero incidents'.

a) cracking through the crown

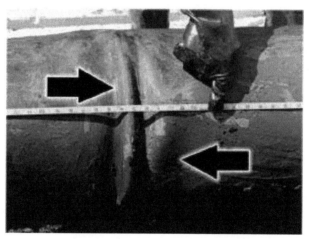

b) view of the buckle prior to removing the coating

Figure 1. Views of a buckle misidentified as a Tee[after44]

Incident experience through 2000

The year 2000 has been identified earlier as a pivotal, with the Regulator mandating inspection-based reassessment shortly thereafter. In view of the GAO's comments[26] that focused concern on aspects of HL Systems, Figure 2 considers accident rates for HL pipelines.

Figure 2a presents a pie chart for onshore crude oil transmission systems parsed as pipelines, stations, and components that is representative over time. The 'pipelines' slice of this pie includes the lineal portion of the system (and its integral components like main-line valves). Pipelines connect to aspects parsed as 'facilities', such as stations and tank farms, and aspects parsed as 'components / equipment', which lie within the fence-line and/or containing berms of those facilities. Figure 2b contrasts HL data for 'pipeline' accidents in the US from before what has been termed the 'vintage' era, well into what comprises modern systems, ending with the year 2000. The notation 'EC' and 'IC' respectively denote external and internal corrosion, 'pipe' and 'welds' reflect features that were not exposed in a mill or pre-service pressure test, while the notation 'TPD' represents incidents due to third-party and outside-forces damage.

Figure 2a indicates that the lineal part of the hazardous liquids system accounted for about one-quarter of the hazardous liquids accidents. The remainder occurred within controlled facilities like tank farms and pumping stations. Under PHMSA's more stringent reporting requirements introduced in 2002[49] the accident frequency that underlies Figure 2b is expected to increase in response to the decreases in the fiscal and volume thresholds, the later dropping to nuisance levels. Trending[48] indicates this change in thresholds can affect a significant increase in the accident rate relative to the years prior, which as expected is evident in independent analysis by Hunton and Williams LLP[50].

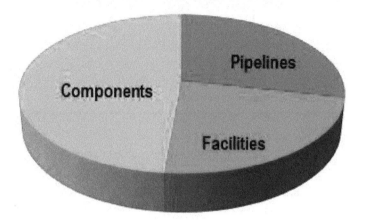

a) parsed by component

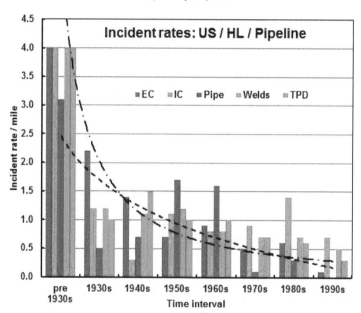

b) incident rate/mile grouped by decade

Figure 2. Incident trends for US HL pipelines.

Trends and their implications through 2000

The y-axis in Figure 2b is accident frequency over the time intervals noted on the x-axis through 2000. As that rate depends on the length of the pipeline involved, as a step toward normalizing this metric the y-axis results have been presented relative to the number of miles reported to exist during that time interval. Accident frequency and mileage were sourced from PHMSA[49], with that mileage data supplemented by results of Kiefner[51] for the period prior to the PHMSA reporting such data. Each of the x-axis intervals is parsed as noted earlier.

The external and internal corrosion are time-dependent processes that are amenable to inspection-based IM that detects and tracks their size and progression over time, such that they can be repaired well before they penetrate the wall as a leak, or reach a critical length typically leading to an axial split. The previously benign pipe and weld features also are amenable to inspection-based IM – provided that the correct tools are run to track their size and growth over time. In contrast, the occurrence of third-party and outside-forces damage are random over time and in location. Such events can be better managed by preventive schemes.

Figure 2b[52] indicates that the largest absolute decrease in accident rate, or increase in apparent safety, came very early in the history of the US pipeline infrastructure – well prior to Federal Regulation and mandated IM that began circa 1970. Those early accidents were associated with the most problematic of the early materials and construction practices, and occurred in areas where upsets or other issues gave rise to features that concentrated the stresses leading to failure. As those problematic practices were recognized, alternatives were developed. The remnant problems represented the more resistant steels and smaller largely benign features – making failures local to those issues less likely. Progress in the steel industry led to Bessemer steels being largely abandoned by 1940. The advent of high-strength low-alloy concepts, and metallurgically clean steels circa the early 1960s was another step improvement in the line pipe. Thermomechanical controlled pro-

cessing and accelerated cooling followed in the late 1970s and continues in use.

By the end of the 1940s, machine-field-bent pipe had largely replaced occasionally problematic schemes like wrinkle-bends. Cou-
plings and collars gave way to oxy-acetylene girth-welds that were soon
displaced by much improved girth-weld practices. 'Orange-peel' fabri-
cations that had been used to create transitions and other fittings gave
way to shop-made transitions. Over-the-ditch coatings also improved,
and CP was implemented. Hydrotesting came into use in the 1950s, the
benefits of which were broadly recognized by the industry, as evident in
work funded by the AGA in the late 1960s[53]. Step improvements continued in the 1970s and beyond, with the introduction of fusion-bond-
ed epoxy coatings, much improved GW technologies and practices,
inspection technologies, and inhibitors. Incremental advances in such
technologies have continued since in aspects such as ILI, in-ditch inspection, aboveground survey technology, protection and contact detection and avoidance schemes, monitoring and control technologies,
(which include leak detection and SCADA (Supervisory Control and
Data Acquisition).[*]

The many improvements in materials and construction practices,
and in coatings and inhibitors, should be manifest in better pipelines.
Improvements in real-time measurement and quality control during
production and construction should lead to fewer process upsets. But,
as upsets can't be precluded, where they might pose a practical concern
they should be weeded out by quality-assurance practices. On this basis, when averaged over intervals as long as 10 years as in Figure 2b,
this figure should show a consistent decrease in the accident rates for
all but TPD. While there is a decline in the overall rate, it is clear that
the results are not consistent over time – even in the period approach-
ing 2000. This implies inconsistencies or inadequacies in the quality
practices, and/or in the inspection and assessment practices, and/or in

---

[*] Given the focus of this Chapter, the brief synopsis over time in this and the prior paragraph does
not seek to be comprehensive in scope or in detail. Such aspects are considered in much greater
detail in References 54 and 55, and in the many citations considered therein.

the maintenance and repair/rehabilitation practices, which need to be identified and rectified.

Trending hazardous liquid pipeline accidents since 2000

Accident frequency shown in Figure 2b is one commonly used metric for the effectiveness of IM practices used in many industries. Footnote 8 notes that the PHMSA refers to reportable events as 'incidents' in reference to natural gas systems, and as 'accidents' in reference to hazardous liquids systems. It should be emphasized that accident frequency as defined by PHMSA and used in Figure 2 is not the same as what might be reported via the media, the public and other stakeholders as a pipeline accident. Without defining criteria, such as PHMSA has done, what might be referred to as an accident ranges from visible release to a major spill, all of which must be traceably documented and openly compiled.

The Internet lists pipeline accidents for the United States[35], and elsewhere worldwide[56]. The list for the US tabulates 'events' termed accidents in intervals longer than 25 years prior to 1950, and in blocks of 25 years from 1950 through 2000. Beginning in 2000[36], and since[37], the number of events listed has sufficed to support yearly reporting. This shift to shorter reporting intervals implies that what are termed accidents: 1) are occurring more frequently; 2) are inconsistently or more stringently defined; and 3) documentation is more broadly available and communication has improved. Of these the first is conceptually in conflict with the improvements noted above in the quality practices, and in the inspection and assessment practices, while the other two can create confusion in trends due to inconsistent definitions and the effects of unrelated factors.

Trending incident frequency indicates that several major pipeline occurrences on the US systems leading up to and during 2000 and implies that the statutory actions in the years just before and soon after were legislative and regulatory reactions to those incidents (e.g.,23,24,57). The critical question in this context is – did the mandated changes that moved pipeline IM toward inspection-based assessment affect a step reduction in incident frequency? As for Figure 2, this question is addressed by trending 'significant' incidents from 2000 through 3/27/2019 using data available from PHMSA as 'pipeline incident 20-year trends'[58], with that outcome shown in Figure 3.

Trending over this interval provides the perspective of 20 years, while minimizing the effects of the transition to more stringent reporting thresholds that occurred in 2002.[59] Significant incidents were considered because this category most closely matches the reportable criteria that underlie Figure 2. Because inspection-based condition assessment has applied to both hazardous liquid and natural gas systems, the effectiveness of this approach is evaluated by pooling the data for both systems.

Figure 3 plots the number of fatalities (front data tier), injuries (middle tier), and occurrences (rear tier) for the significant incidents for each of the years up through the present.

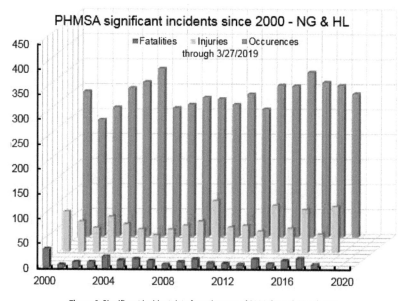

Figure 3. Significant incident data from the start of 2000 through March 2019

Considering the front data tier in Figure 3 it is apparent that the year 2000 stands out as the worst by far among the years that have followed in regard to fatalities. While not evident from these results, it also stands out in comparison the prior years, but is not the worst among them. All else being equal in terms of cleanup/mitigation and other cost metrics, it is likely that 2000 also would be among the worst, if not the worst, in regard to consequences.

Effectiveness of inspection-based condition assessment since 2000

While the year 2000 stands out in terms of fatalities (the front tier), the expectation that the mandated changes in the IM process would affect a reduction in incident frequency is not supported by the trends shown in Figure 3. For example, consider the mid-tier data in Figure 3, which represent injuries. Therein it is evident that such occurrences tend to be increasing since 2000, as the time-weighted average for the last half of this dataset is larger than that for the first half. Thus, at least in this context, the practice of inspection-based IM has not affected the desired reduction in the number of injuries. Moreover, it has not brought about a reduction in the number of occurrences over this time interval, which is evident from the rear-tier dataset.

It follows in view of Figures 2 and 3 that the historic and current IM practices are tending to a state of diminishing returns. In spite of expanding inspection and maintenance budgets, Figure 3 indicates little to no reduction in these key stakeholder metrics over the last almost two decades! The next section considers aspects of the ILI tools and process, and the IM condition assessment practices, as plausible causes for the above-noted trends.

Concerns with inspection-based condition assessment practices

Given that Figure 3 does not clearly demonstrate the merits of inspection-based condition assessment, whereas it was expected or hoped to, it is instructive to consider the key elements of this IM approach to understand why. Based on that outcome two plausible explanations are evaluated. First, the possibility that this approach to IM is faulty is considered. Thereafter, the possibility that the apparent shortcomings of condition-based IM trace to faulted implementation is considered in light of how/why pipelines fail.

How and why pipeline failures occur[*]

Failure localized at defects typically occurs in pipelines either by plastic collapse or by fracture, with the properties, the loads, and the pipe's geometry combining to determine the controlling failure mechanism, and the sizes of the defects that will fail at a given pressure. Tougher steels will blunt initially sharp defects, leading to collapse-controlled failure that will occur at a higher pressure compared to fracture-controlled failure – all else being equal.

Whether or not failure occurs depends on the balance between the drivers for failure, which involves the loads (used here generically) and the defect size, shape, and orientation, and the local resistance, which is quantified by the local properties, specifically the collapse stress ($\approx$ the ultimate tensile stress, UTS) and the toughness. Thus, failure does not occur selectively at the largest anomaly. Rather, it occurs where the balance between the drivers and the resistance tips in favor of collapse or fracture. Physical support for this observation can be found in the results of full-scale testing wherein failures occasionally occur remote to the 'worst-case' defect whereby the test's design failure was anticipated – occasionally the largest defect does not control.

It follows in this context that we need a broader inspection-based condition assessment process than is currently available – which will remain the case until we can more broadly characterize all relevant loads and more critically quantify the local metrics of the resistance. Concerns in this context can trace to the inspection as well as the condition assessment.

---

[*]   Aspects of why pipelines fail are broadly discussed in Reference 60 where details of the mechanisms that underlie such failures can be accessed via QR Codes.

Condition assessment in perspective

Practical technology to assess the effects of blunt as well as sharp features in pressure boundaries like a pipeline dates to work done in regarding rocket and aerospace applications beginning from about 1950, but much earlier if only blunt features are considered. Much work has been done since 2000 regarding fracture mechanics and plastic collapse. As this can be found by Internet web-crawl, such details are left for the reader to pursue. The criteria and models noted earlier quantify the response of pipelines for cases involving blunt features that failed by net-section (plastic) collapse. These included the Level 13 criterion that led to B31G6 circa 1984. Thereafter Modified B31G7 emerged in 1989, as did the algorithm that became RSTRENG8. That algorithm repetitively applied Modified B31G along the path connecting the deepest segments of metal loss within complex corrosion, to identify the worst-case failure pressure. As it was coded as software RSTRENG is considered a Level 2 method. These early assessment tools embedded empirical calibrations involving the lower-strength pipe grades. It became evident in their application to testing of metal-loss in higher strength pipes they were considered overly conservative, and so augmented in the 1990s by technology like PCORRC9, LPC-110, and Cor-LAS11. These 1990s developments were rooted in FEA, whose results were trended to develop equations and software (i.e., Levels 1 and 2) to manage metal-loss in pipelines made of the higher-strength line-pipe Grades.

Empirically based technology that became known as the NG-18[*] Equations was also available beginning in the 1970s to assess sharp crack-like features, whose failure was controlled by collapse and/or by fracture[12], while a fracture-mechanics (FM) based scheme emerged from work that began in the mid-1980s, which became the PRCI ductile-flaw-growth model (DFGM)[13]. This early fracture-based technolo-

---

[*] 'NG-18' makes reference to work done under the guidance of the Pipeline Research Committee (PRC) of AGA, which later became the NG-18 Project Supervisory Committee. See Reference 60 for further background.

gy was later integrated with a collapse-controlled model and coded as a Level 2 criterion in an updated version[14] of the software first released as pipeline axial-flaw failure criterion (PAFFC). CorLAS11 also can be used to assess cracking.

Isolated idealized features vs reality and multiple adjacent features

The empirical calibration basis of the 1970s and early 1980s technology determines the applicability of these Level 1 tools, whereas the assumptions and idealizations that underlay the FEA and FM models define the applicability of the Level 2 and Level 3 schemes. As net-section collapse depends on the cross-sectional area lost due to corrosion or other causes, such failure through relatively complex corrosion depends simply on the area lost. As the 'shape factor' used in the B31G family of criteria was quantified relative to the area lost, both B31G and Modified B31G were viable in applications to metal-loss features over the scope that underlay their empirical calibration. But, as their use broadened, software known as RSTRENG was introduced to better account for more complex adjacent features. RSTRENG tends to provide conservative predictions, which can at times be more conservative than hoped for. Note that the resistance to plastic collapse, which occurs with the onset of necking, is reasonably approximated by the UTS.

In contrast to cases where NSC controls failure, and area-lost generally suffices to characterize feature shape, feature shape for FM and fracture-controlled failures is characterized in terms of the anomaly's orientation, length, depth, and shape. The resistance metrics for fracture generally uncouple crack initiation and propagation, with those properties in some cases showing strong gradients across areas like seam and girth welds.

As FM models are typically developed in regard to a single (isolated) feature, and often assume a semi-elliptic in shape, it follows that Level 2 models that embed these idealizations will struggle to manage field cracking, which seldom is isolated but rather lies coplanar or otherwise sits adjacent to other features. An exception to this has been noted in cases where a single crack is clearly dominant among overlapping adjacent almost collinear features. This is schematically illustrated in Figure 4 in terms of crack-front profiles traced from a macrofracto-graph of some stress-corrosion cracking (SCC). Detailed fractography using scanning electron microscopy (SEM) indicated that all features contained smaller thumbnail origins and indicated that the smaller features nearby the deep dominant crack showed evidence of multiple sympathetic nucleation due to the presence of the deep crack. Failure predictions in this case considering the deeper feature to be isolated reasonably matched the hydrotest pressure local to this failure, which split the pipe body many feet (~2m) in rather low toughness line pipe.

While interaction and other complexities can be quantified via FM[61,62], little beyond that noted exists to manage the scope of features that can be found in the field. Absent the needed technology to deal simply with the complexities of field cracking, past work involving such features has relied on case-by-case adaptation of FM, which has led to viable blind predictions for field cracking. For example, the PRCI DFGM coupled with rudimentary collapse analyses was done in re-sponding to an information request during the Canadian NEB SCC Hearing. This blind analysis led to excellent predictions of the failure behavior for SCC that had caused a number of pipeline ruptures[63]. Sim-ilar quality predictions involving ERW seam features follow next in the discussion of Figure 5 that reinforce this observation – specifically in regard to Figure 5b.

Key to the just noted blind predictive success was the case-by-case subject-matter expert (SME) analyses that sought to account for the differences in crack driving force for the idealized feature vs that for complex cracking. In contrast, absent such adaptation the predictive results show, as expected, lower quality[64]. Figure 5 has been developed from images shown in Reference 65 to illustrate predictive quality in terms of model complexity and the need for viable application-specific model inputs. Figure 5a shows Level 1 predictions whereas Figure 5b presents Level 2 predictions, which as required considered the shape of the defect and developed case-specific properties – which can be critical when dealing with ERW seams.* Such results make clear that quality predictions with little scatter can be achieved, but with some effort when assessing field features.

The conclusion is clear in contrasting these images: successful evaluation of the outputs from an ILI run requires quality inputs for all aspects of a given predictive model. While the differences evident in these figures trace in part to the models, independent analyses specific to PAFFC indicates that much of the error evident traces to the quality of the inputs – with the same being the case for any assessment model. While nominal properties might suffice to characterize the pipe's local resistance to plastic collapse based on the UTS, this is much less likely for fracture-controlled situations. While as evident above field complexities can be managed case by case by a SME, unfortunately viable Level 2 FM schemes have not been developed by the industry to reduce such work to a Level 2 model – other than by adapting a deepest-path analog to RSTRENG (which if area-based assumes that collapse controls the failure – not fracture).

In summary, regarding idealize shape it is noted that most Level 1 and some Level 2 approaches do not adequately quantify the interaction between mutually adjacent features that are separated by the order of a full-wall thickness or less. Rather, conservative interaction rules are adopted, such as those used by the vendors when "boxing" features. Improvements in this context are essential in adapting the current assessment tools to better manage the anomalies in pipelines.

Figure 4. Shaded crack profiles illustrative of a 'dominant' crack (with adjacent SCC)

---

* Note, as well, part a) reflects nominal properties whereas part b) reflects properties determined specific to the pipe-pups used in full-scale testing of pipe sections with anomalies that had been removed from service.

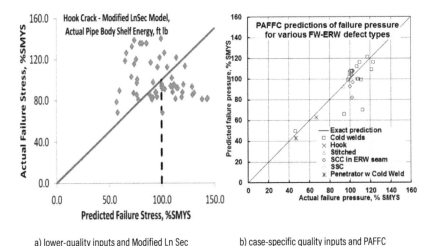

a) lower-quality inputs and Modified Ln Sec   b) case-specific quality inputs and PAFFC

Figure 5. Comparison of predictive results[65]

Trends in collapse and fracture controlled failures

What follows considers predictions made for isolated part-through-wall cracking that reasonably matched the assumptions that underlie PAFFC Release IV. While Figure 5b implies its validity in such cases, because its validation establishes credibility for the trending, discussion, and implications that follow, there is value in further considering its validity in applications to failure predictions for such features in full-scale testing. Appendix A7 in Reference 15 evaluated the then available full-scale test database as the benchmark to quantify the viability of the collapse and fracture models for isolated defects that subsequently led to Release IV of PAFFC. That model was validated for a range of isolated defect shapes and sizes in pipe diameters ranging from 8 inches (203 mm) to 42 inches (1067 mm) for diameter to thickness ratios ranging from ~35 through 110, for grades ranging from B through X80, and for lower-toughness steels up through plastic collapse conditions, in steels whose CVN energy was as high as 200 ft-lb (270J).With model credibility established, some representative predicted failure boundaries and their practical implications are discussed in regard to Figure 6.

The y-axis in this figure presents failure pressure that has been normalized relative to SMYS. The corresponding failing defect length is shown on the x-axis, whereas defect depths up to 90% through-wall (TW) are presented as contours referenced to depth normalized by the nominal wall thickness, which is shown on the right margin of the figure. These predicted boundaries reflect the response of initially sharp axial defects in ERW-seamed pipe nominally 16.125 by 0.250 inch (410 x 6.35 mm) with a wall made of X52 (Gr 359) that are subjected to increasing pressure. Given the measured range of body and seam properties, Figure 6a has been developed for (full-size equivalent, FSE) CVN plateau energy (CVP) of 5 ft-lb (~6.8 J), while Figure 6b has been developed for 20 ft-lb (~27.1 J)[*]. As normalized parameters are involved, care must be taken when using such boundaries in cases where actual yield and the wall thickness differ significantly from nominal.

Two heavy trends are also included in each part of Figure 6, which run diagonally down toward the lower right-hand corner of these figures. These trends reflect the predicted onset of TW tearing (the lower of these lines) and TW instability (the upper line) – the latter discriminating between leak and rupture. Collapse controlled failures are easily identified in such plots, because net-section collapse leads to nested smooth contours as a function of depth. The boundaries shown for the higher-toughness case at d/t =0.1 and much of that at d/t = 0.2 illustrate this trait. The transition to fracture control is evident where the nested boundaries break downward from their characteristic nested trends. This is evident for the boundary at d/t =0.2 at lengths larger than about 12 inches (~305 mm). Because both defect length as well as depth control fracture, the nested smooth boundaries evident as a function of depth for collapse give way to fracture controlled boundaries that lack that do not develop nested evenly spaced failure boundaries.

---

[*] The use of 'plateau' energy is relevant for ductile response, which means that the mode of failure will be fully ductile (i.e., 100% shear area for non-rising shelf steels). As these failure boundaries show, fully ductile fracture response does not always translate to collapse controlled failure.

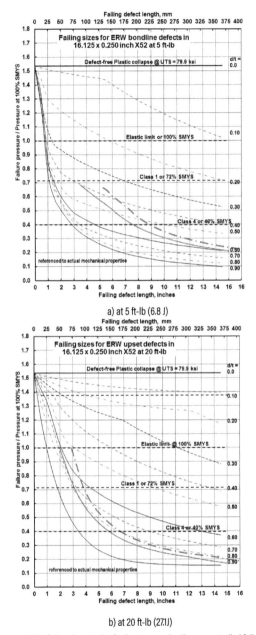

a) at 5 ft-lb (6.8 J)

b) at 20 ft-lb (27.1J)

Figure 6. Representative failure boundaries for fracture- and collapse-controlled failure[39]

Because toughness does not alter the collapse-controlled response of a given size feature in the same pipe, any collapse-controlled failure boundaries in Figure 6b would be identical to that shown in Figure 6a at a given depth. As relatively lower toughness levels are being compared in Figure 6, replicated trends indicating collapse control are evident only for shorter defects at shallow normalized depths. The results for the higher toughness indicate a shift in the failure response from fracture toward collapse controlled failure. This transition is evident by comparing the failure boundaries shown in Figure 6b (20 ft-lb, ~27.1 J) depth by depth to those in Figure 6a (5 ft-lb, ~6.8 J). The major differences in the failure pressures and failing defect sizes that develop between some of these boundaries indicate that for these cases a 15 ft-lb (~20.3 J) change in CVN can affect large difference in failing defect sizes.

In view of the strong differences in failure pressures and failing defect sizes due to a 15 ft-lb (~20.3 J) difference in CVN energy it is instructive to review the resistance to failure in terms of CVN energy, to establish the range of CVN energies that might be found between adjacent line pipes or within the seam in a joint of line pipe. Figure 7 presents full-range T-L CVN data for adjacent pipe joints in part a), whereas part b) presents data for testing in close proximity across what was a 'sound' seam. The data in part a) represent triplicate testing done on samples from hot-tap coupons cut from 1962 low-frequency (LF) ERW production of 20-inch (508 mm) diameter X52 line pipe. The y-axes are respectively CVN energy (left) and shear area (right). As dual units cannot be so presented, to assist regarding SI units 35 ft-lb on the y-axis corresponds to 47J, and the limits on the x-axis transform to -73.3° and 93.3°C. The 50% shear-area transition temperature (SATT) for these steels is by inspection ~25°F which corresponds to ~3.9°C. The data shown in part b) are on similar coordinates, except that here the results reflect testing in the pipe body (denoted BM), as well as within the seam upset and the bondline.

It is apparent from Figure 7a that the resistance values on the lower-shelf (brittle) or the upper-shelf (plateau, fully ductile) do not differ significantly as compared to the 15 ft-lb (~20.3 J) difference considered in Figure 6. But, as is usual for such testing, within the transition between these show differences in CVN energy that could affect large differences in failing defect sizes, and so affect shifts between collapse and fracture control. If a pipeline operates well above the SATT for the pipe steel, such variability is not a concern. Because steels produced after the early 1960s were developed and selected to ensure that pipeline operation, even during upsets, was well above the SATT, concern for such variability is usually limited to earlier construction.

Such cannot be said regarding possible cracking within an ERW seam, and welds in general, because the thermal cycle(s) (and where involved mechanical loading) of that process affect strong changes in the BM microstructure within the upset. The trends in Figure 7b indicate that such microstructural changes can affect large differences in the cracking resistance regardless of operating temperature for the scenarios considered. While the results shown were developed across a flash-welded seam in 1955 A O Smith production, such trends have been evident in seams for many producers over the years, and are not unique to LF ERW.

Some Assessment Gaps. Experience indicates that some important gaps remain to be bridged in regard to assessment, three of which follow.

The first gap involves interacting and adjacent features – specifically discriminating between them and characterizing their sizes, shapes, and tip to tip positions, and eventually also how this detail gets reported. Such details are needed to determine if features in close proximity can interact and coalesce, which can cause an immediate step increase in the length of the feature. This could lead to a rupture in lieu of a leak. More critically, this step increase has the potential to cause failure well before the effects of the growth rate over time would indicate failure.

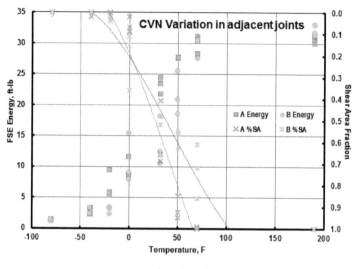

a) within adjacent joints

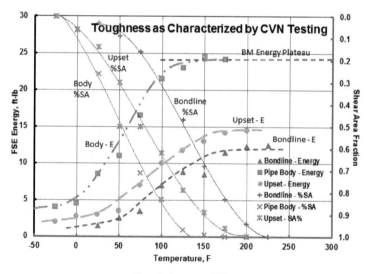

b) gradient across an ERW seam

Figure 7. Trends in CVN energy in line pipe and ERW seams[66]

The second gap involves the determination of local properties and their spatial gradients, as develops for example across a seam weld. It can be simply illustrated in regard to EWR seams with a sound bondline wherein the upset contains features identified by ILI as hook cracks – which are due to dirty steel and so can occur in modern as well as vintage seams. While hook cracks can pose issues, the toughness in the upset can be many times that in the bondline, which in light of Figure 6 means that in such cases features in the upset are less are much less prone to fail – all else being equal. Unfortunately, such feature and positional discrimination is not yet available via ILI such that digs and rehab with marginal value must be done to limit the chance for bondline failure.

The third gap involves aspects of how feature sizes and orientations are reported in contrast to how this information is used in condition assessment. One aspect with strong IM implications involves feature length, which is reported as the length that corresponds to the detection threshold depth. This is broadly considered later in the section leading to Some Compatibility Gaps.

Inspection in perspective

History tracks how we arrived at the current state, and the challenges faced, whose resolution was guided by the apparent needs (market demands) and constrained by the available technology. Geoff Foreman considered the history and evolution of pipeline inspection earlier. What follows focuses on aspects specific to the convergence of inspection and assessment, and the compatibility between the inspection outputs and the present-day needs of assessment.

Today we enjoy the benefits of computer speed and storage, miniaturization, and portable high-energy-density batteries, to name a few that have been key in the evolution of inspection technologies. As Foreman writes, today we have access to a broad range of sensor technologies that continue to evolve to better detect and size a broader range of features. Sensor spacing is decreasing, with their output captured over shorter intervals, so we benefit* from spatially dense data that better characterize features. This drives improved accuracy and reduced uncertainty in sync with the market and as technology facilitates.

Since the mid-1990s what used to be termed metal-loss has been divided into seven categories depending on the features' planar dimensions and depth, which have been sensed for many years at 'high-resolution'. 'Combo' tools also began to emerge about that time, with the benefit of gathering data for more than one major feature type in a single tool run. 'Big data' has since in various ways become an industry focus that coupled with combo tools opens to benefits such as improved signal interpretation and alignment between feature types.[67] Finally, tool runs are being validated, and a much broader more reliable set of in-ditch tools is available to support that process. Key in this context, specifications and other guidance have been developed to codify minimum practices from run preparation through run validation.[68-70]

Tool development over the decades since the late 1950s provides a benchmark against which to judge the just-noted evolution of ILI tools. During the early decades only MFL and caliper tools were available. Storage, data recording, and other technology constraints limited the volume of information that could be captured, as well as how it was captured, and how it was recorded. For such reasons the early caliper tools (TDW) tracked a single data channel[67], and initially recorded only the largest shape deviation over the course of the run. These tools used mechanical finger-sensors to track around the pipe's circumference, averaging what they sense through a polymeric shroud. As evident in Figure 8 (photo circa 1991), this now multichannel tool combined the drive, power, electronics and storage, odometer wheels, and sensors within a single free-swimming platform that was just several feet (~ meter) in length. The displacements sensed through the shroud quantified physical changes in the pipe's shape that were calibrated directly in length dimensions.

---

* Such traits are generally feature specific.

Figure 8. View of the sensor end of the caliper tool circa 1991: image courtesy TDW

Multichannel sensing and recording was implemented as MFL tools developed, with the sensors (number of channels) then being rather widely spaced. By the mid-1980s 24 channels were being sensed and recorded on what is considered a low-resolution tool. Figure 9 illustrates the data channels as recorded (specific to the Linalog MFL tool[71]). The sensors are now tightly spaced circumferentially – with the utility of ILI being greatly increased as the sensors and related electronics was miniaturized and the data storage capacity increased along with the energy density of the batteries.

Whereas the output of a caliper or deformation tool could be directly calibrated relative to some benchmark length, the output of a MFL tool local to a metal loss feature reflects the local change it causes in the magnetic field (flux-leakage). While such occurrences can be identified, as evident in record shown in Figure 9, relating this output to the size and shape of the metal-loss is less simple, as there was no direct benchmark calibration. In the mid-1980s the flux-leakage was recorded reel-to-reel on magnetic tape, along with the tool's speed, orientation, and location in the pipeline – with magnetic markers attached to the line periodically to benchmark the tool's position. At the end of the run the tool was recovered and the analog record fed to a strip chart recorder. That record was then 'read' by an experienced analyst, and Graded 1, 2, or 3, for which severity (depth) increased moving from 1 (15 to 30% penetration) up to 3 (over 50% penetration), within ± 10% by reporting category. As this interpretation then was manual and human factors could be in play, this Grading took time, and was subject to the interpreter's experience, physical and/or mental fatigue, and other factors.

Misinterpretation, accuracy and uncertainty, and utility. While step improvements have continued over the decades, the sensor output from even current ILI tools is from time to time misinterpreted – leading to miscalls of anomaly identification, size, location, and orientation. Figure 2 served to emphasize this, wherein a relatively high-aspect-ratio buckle was reportedly called a Tee-fitting! While miscalls can open to issues in condition assessment, the usual error caveat for high-resolution MFL tools 'accurate within ±10% with 80% confidence' indicates that the output of such tools provides a viable foundation for IM – provided the error-band is considered. Perhaps as important are issues involving false-positive calls, which can open to expense without a corresponding benefit, and false-negative calls, which mean potentially problematic features are missed in the inspection. While these aspects have not been quantified in this book, a chapter in the book *Oil and Gas Pipelines: Integrity and Safety Handbook*, "Mechanical Damage in Pipelines: A Review of the Methods and Improvements in Characterization, Evaluation, and Mitigation" addresses such details, and validation of tool runs.[72]

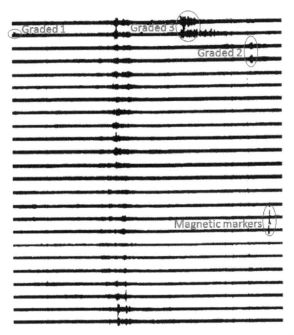

Figure 9. Compressed illustration of a 24-channel Linalog output, circa mid-1980s[after 71]

Practical utility, in-ditch digs, and tool / run verification / validation. The perspective of history is also instructive here. As the early tools were developed they provided rather course measures of the features, for example graded depths. Given their limited sensitivity, the uncertainty in the output from those early tool runs simply supplemented the IM practices of the day. In contrast, for inspection-based condition assessment the inspection output becomes the foundation for the assessment. Prior to inspection as the foundation for IM, a tool run simply provided 'insight' into pipeline condition. This is clearly evident in marketing catchphrases like "get to know your pipeline better."[71] In lieu of success stories on vendor websites, and/or tool specifications, the utility of the tool in early runs was justified simply by their inspection experience. For example, into the mid-1980s marketing brochures can be found[71] that cite years of service and the number of miles (kilometers) they had 'surveyed'. Tool thresholds and claimed capabilities only emerged in the 1990s, as competition developed and the demand for tool runs was still limited, as this had not yet been (indirectly) mandated.

Faced with decisions regarding vendor and tool selection, by the mid-1990s pipeline operators organized the Pipeline Operators Forum (POF) as an informal setting for pipeline integrity engineers to share and/or build best practices for continuing improvement of the IM process. The initial POF Specification was released in 1996[68], which dealt with the process and its reporting. Even so, history indicates that disparities developed between the Vendor's claims/specified performance and the outcome of the ILI process. Cleaning the line was recognized as a first-run success factor, and the so-called 'unity plot' became a regular feature in ILI-related papers and forums. As the unity plot presented a one-to-one comparison of the inspection results and a 'benchmark,' then depending on the in-ditch benchmark and many other factors there were potential uncertainties embedded in both axes of the plot. Depending on the skill of the in-ditch technician and the capabilities of his tools/sensors the quality of the benchmark results could be worse than that for the ILI run[73]. In addition, depending on the nature of the feature and the operational circumstances during the dig, the in-ditch results could be affected by differences in temperature and pressure, as well as by differences affected by exposing the pipeline. Thus, it is not surprising that a 2013 review of ILI run successes by Kiefner et al[38] on occasion notes "the inspection and follow-up field NDE (non-destructive examination) were insufficient to conclude that the seam integrity had been verified." That report also noted successes for which the ILI results were considered a viable basis to assure integrity. Given the need to assure integrity, run and tool verification / validation have become integral to the ILI process, and are now elements of Specifications[69] and Standards[70]. In closure, it must be noted that when making decisions the certainty of the outcomes and the effects of tool performance become key considerations in the effectiveness of inspection-based IM[74] and so also its ability to affect a continuing reduction in incident frequency.

Considerations in the use of inspection-based IM

While miscalls can open to issues in condition assessment, the usual error caveat for high-resolution MFL tools 'accurate within ±10% with 80% confidence' also should be considered, as it can affect significant swings in the failure pressure. In turn, this can affect a decrease in the margin of safety anticipated following an ILI run. The potential significance of these aspects is illustrated in Figure 6, which quantified the response of initially sharp defects.*

Interplay between error bands and failing defect sizes. Inspection of Figure 6a indicates that at 5 ft-lb (6.8 J) and a pressure corresponding to 100% of the specified minimum yield stress (SMYS) a ±10% swing in defect size causes a swing in failure pressure of more than ±8%, such that this error tolerance could be as large as ~±134 psi (~922 kPa). For the corresponding scenario at 5 ft-lb (6.8 J) and a pressure at 40% SMYS a ±10% swing in defect size is associated with close to a ±3.5% swing in failure pressure, which corresponds to a pressure swing the order of ±56 psi (~389 kPa). The effects of this error tolerance are reversed at 20 ft-lb (27.1 J), which causes a transition for many of the defect sizes to collapse controlled failure, which is independent of toughness. At 20 ft-lb (27.1 J) and a pressure of 100% SMYS inspection of Figure 6b indicates that a ±10% swing in defect size leads to swing in failure pressure as large as ±7%, or the order of ±113 psi (~778 kPa). In contrast, at 20 ft-lb (27.1 J) and a pressure of 40% SMYS a ±10% swing in defect size is close to a ±2.8% swing in failure pressure, such that this error tolerance corresponds to about ±45 psi (~308 kPa).

It follows that the error tolerance can affect significant swings in failure pressure[15]. It is also evident that toughness can affect significant differences in the effects of the error tolerance and can alter the cir-

---

* The error-band noted is specific to blunt features whereas Figure 6 was introduced in regard to initially sharp defects. The intent here is not to comingle these aspects, but rather to broadly illustrate the implications of such bands. Thus, the viability of this discussion and the related conclusions are specific to the response shown in Figure 6, whose validity was discussed above in regard to SCC and anomalies in ERW seams.

cumstances most sensitive to it. Moreover, it is evident that toughness is a first-order driver for these failure boundaries, with sizing accuracy and so also precision potentially being secondary to the role of toughness in IM decisions depending on the circumstances.

Aspects of functionality. Functionality of the inspection platform and its sensors contribute to the viability of inspection-based IM, and its ability to reduce the incident frequency.

The interior of a pipeline is not always smooth and round, nor is it always clean. The profiles of girth and long seam welds protrude into what elsewhere is nominally smooth and round when pressurized. While many ERW seams are nominally scarfed to near the full pipe wall thickness, such is not always the case, particularly in earlier construction. The seam reinforcement of longitudinal and girth welds likewise protrudes into the pipe's inside diameter (ID). Figures 7b and 7c show examples of protruding ERW seams in contrast to a closely scarfed ID in the offset seam of Figure 7a.

Whereas the profiles of double submerged arc welded (DSAW) long seams or those produced via modern GW practices are more or less consistent, the lift-off that occurs in such ERW/FW seams differs joint-to-joint within a pipeline, as well as pipeline-to-pipeline. This can complicate managing their effects, with adverse impacts on data quality. While some sensors are designed to sense local differences in pipe shape, others are not. Lift-off for MFL tools also affects differences in the magnetic field. Tool speed out-of-range is another aspect of functionality that adversely affects data quality, as have issues with the odometer wheels. Finally, it must be emphasized that the viability of a tool run is dependent on line cleanliness, which in turn can depend on the transported product, the operating conditions of the pipeline, and other factors.

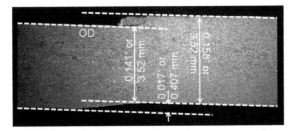

a) offset and scarfed

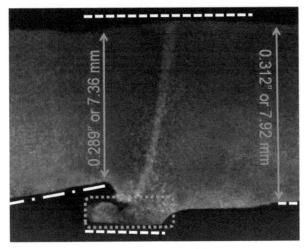

b) offset, under- scarfed

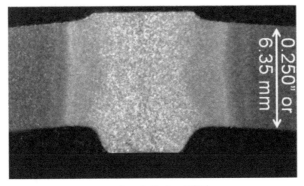

c) scarfed flash weld (FW)

Figure 10. Some causes of lift-off, which here are specific to ERW/FW long seams

While functionality issues can adversely affect data quality, perhaps the most critical facet of functionality involves matching the sensor technology and tool platform to the pipeline, and the types of features that are known, or might be active in the pipeline. Obviously, a tool run to characterize metal loss does little to ensure integrity when the pending failure reflects, for example, the presence of active stress corrosion cracking or selective seam-weld corrosion.

Functionality has greatly benefited from miniaturization, increased data capacity, battery energy density, and the development of multi-technology tools and the use of multiple datasets. All such developments contribute to enhanced data quality, and so enhanced certainty in related IM decisions – provided that the data can be processed, integrated, and assimilated effectively. Not only has the number of data channels increased around the pipeline's circumference, but such data is being captured fast enough to provide a refined spatial characterization of pipeline condition in polar or x-y-z coordinates. Fast-forwarding from the coarse map of metal-loss depth that is evident in Figure 9 to today's technology leads us to 'big data' whose potential yet remains to be fully tapped.

Some inspection gaps. Experience indicates that some important gaps remain to be bridged, three of these follow.

The first gap involves interacting and adjacent features – specifically discrimination between them and characterizing their sizes, shapes, and tip-to-tip positions, and eventually how this detail gets reported. Such details are needed to determine if features in close proximity can interact and coalesce, which can cause an immediate step increase in the length of the feature. This could lead to a rupture in lieu of a leak. More critically, this step increase has the potential to cause failure well before the growth rate would imply its occurrence.

The second gap involves the interplay between assessment and inspection, and the need for inspection tools to improve spatial discrimination so differences in local properties that can develop in welds can be considered in IM decisions. This significance of this gap can be simply illustrated in regard to EWR seams with a sound bondline wherein the upset contains features identified by ILI as hook cracks. While hook cracks can pose issues, the toughness in the upset can be many times that in the bondline, which in light of Figure 6 means that in such cases features in the upset are less are much less prone to burst – all else being equal. Unfortunately, such feature and positional discrimination is not yet available via ILI such that digs and rehab with marginal value must be done to limit the chance for a bondline failure.

The third gap involves aspects of how feature sizes and orientations are reported in contrast to how this information is used in condition assessment. One aspect with strong IM implications involves feature length reported as the length that corresponds to the detection threshold depth, which is considered next.

Compatibility between the inspection and assessment tools

Ideally, the inputs to condition assessment / FFS analyses would be directly quantified from the output of the inspection process and its report, such that this information could be seamlessly imported into condition assessment tools. This requires compatibility between the output from the inspection technology and the input to the defect-severity models. Failure in this compatibility limits the ability of inspection-based IM to reduce the incident frequency. Depending on the shape of the feature, length as reported corresponding to the threshold depth as shown in Figure 11a could closely match the surface-breaking (actual) length, but as will be clear shortly, it equally could be very different. It becomes apparent that the significance of this length difference can strongly affect the threat posed by an anomaly, as illustrated next in view of Figure 11b, and the failure boundaries shown earlier in Figure 6.

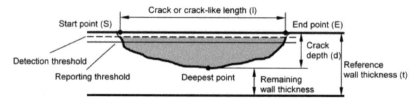

a) crack length (POF Figure 2.9)

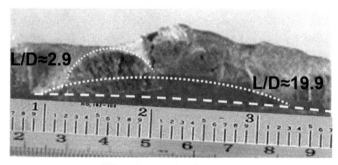

b) illustrating two quite different L/D cracks

Figure 11. Aspects of cracking as reported and in reality

The cracking shown in Figure 11b was chosen in part because it illustrates complex interacting cracking, and in part because this cracking lies toward the extremes in the aspect ratios observed for SCC. The dotted lines approximate the boundaries of a long shallow crack, and that for a deep short crack. The detection threshold (see Figure 11a) cited for some crack tools at one mm, or 0.04 inch falls 13% below the surface of this nominally 0.312 inch (7.92 mm) thick pipe. While this is a small percentage of the wall, the length error for the longer cracking can significantly alter the conclusions of a FFS analysis, as follows.

Inspection of the crack shapes in Figure 11b indicates that if the metal-loss and/or cracking involves aspect ratios (length, L over depth, D) whose values are small, then the defect-length at the threshold depth can be close to the actual length. The short, deep feature toward the left side of this image has an aspect ratio of ~2.9. In contrast, because the reporting threshold in this case lies 13% of the wall below the surface, and this crack has a much flatter shape, the aspect ratio is 19.8, which is quite high. In such cases the actual length is underreported to a much greater extent. As Figure 12 a indicates, high aspect ratio cracking is not uncommon for SCC, such that situations like this could recur frequently, with the extent of the sizing error dependent on L/D. As implied above, at the smaller aspect ratio, the error due to use of threshold rather than surface-breaking length is physically very small. In reference to wall thicknesses typical of transmission pipelines, the corresponding lengths of low-aspect-ratio pits or cracks are less than an inch (~2.5 cm). As evident from Figure 6, in spite of causing just a small error in length, the failure pressure can be very sensitive to this error at short lengths. This sensitivity means that a very small length error can translate into large differences in failure pressure. Comparing the trends in Figures 6a and 6b it also is apparent that toughness can be a determining factor in the significance of this physically small error. While the length error is small for low aspect ratio features, such is not the case where the cracking leads to higher aspect ratios, the implications of which follow.

If the features shown in Figure 11b were detected and sized exactly as they appear on this fracture surface[*], then their reported depths, D, and lengths, L, would match the actual depths measured in regard to the pipe's surface. In cm units these were respectively measured at 1.22 and 2.25 for the shorter crack and 0.48 and 6.19 for the longer crack, which lead to the aspect ratios noted in the figure. As the shorter thumbnail feature has an aspect ratio that is close to semicircular, its threshold length at 1.13 cm is close to the actual surface length, whereas if the depth was reported relative to where that length is measured its value would equate to the actual depth minus the threshold depth. The length error at the threshold depth is just 0.06 cm, or ~3% for this shorter feature. If geometrically similar cracking had developed in the pipeline whose failure response is characterized by Figure 6a, then due to the strong sensitivity to length for short cracking, this trivial length

---

[*] Given the angle to fracture surface that this image was captured at to gain perspective, physical depths in the image differ relative to those on the fracture plane, which underlie the dimensions discussed.

error leads to a nonconservative error in failure pressure well in excess of 100 psi (669 kPa). In contrast, for the tougher pipe considered in Figure 6b the effects of this error are somewhat less, as for tougher steels the sensitivity to length shifts to longer features and also shows a stronger depth dependence.

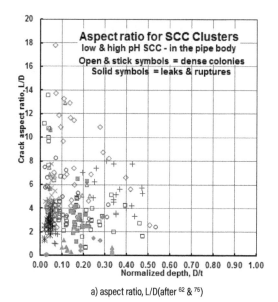

a) aspect ratio, L/D(after [62] & [75])

b) colony showing a range of cracking traits (wet MPI)

Figure 12. Aspects of external SCC on transmission pipelines.

Consider now areal corrosion, and/or stress-corrosion cracking for which the features formed are long compared to their depth, which for present purposes are represented by the high-aspect-ratio feature in Figure 13b. The error in the threshold (i.e., reported ILI) length vs the actual length for this crack is about 10 times that for the shorter feature, but in relative terms is just three times larger due to the much longer length of this feature. If geometrically similar cracking had developed in the pipeline that was characterized by Figure 6a, then due to the strong sensitivity to length for such short cracking, this trivial length error translates to a nonconservative error in failure pressure of about 80 psi (~550kPa). For the tougher pipe considered in Figure 6b the effects of this error are roughly one-fifth of that for the shorter defect in the lower-toughness pipe, whereas for the longer feature the error in failure pressure is about three times that for the shorter feature. These nontrivial nonconservative errors in failure pressure for cracking reflect the sensitivity of the failure boundaries on toughness as a function of L and D^*.

Inspection of Figure 12a indicates that the features found in SCC colonies remote to leaks and ruptures are not too different in normalized terms from those found along leaks and ruptures, except that the scale of their crack depths differs. The crack populations that underlie this figure represent a wide range of toughness, running from collapse through fracture-controlled failures, some involving quite low toughness steels. Moreover, these data reflect leaks and ruptures for hydrotests as well as in-service events where the failures occurred at lower pressures. Cracking becomes critical at lower toughness all else being equal, such that sizing errors become practically more significant for inspections involving lower-toughness steels.

Figure 12b illustrates cracking typical of what can be found in colonies of external SCC on pipelines. Due to the role of toughness the traits evident in such colonies could represent longer deeper coalesced

---

* It has been suggested that the "length error" could be offset by a correction that was referenced to a "typical" value of the aspect ratio. That said, the range in the values of L/D evident in Figure 12a as a function of depth indicates that such inference opens to significant uncertainty.

cracking, through cases for which the critical lengths are the order of a few inches (several cm). Currently, cracking tools tend to be challenged in discriminating between overlapping cracks, and in discerning their individual lengths and depths. The relative importance of accurately identifying and sizing cracking becomes evident in view of the failure boundaries discussed earlier in regard to Figure 6.

Some compatibility gaps

The discussion to this point opens to some important gaps that remain to be bridged, three of which follow.

The first gap involves the uncertainty in sizing error that develops from the disparity between length reported at the threshold depth and the actual length. This uncertainty is compounded by the range of underestimated of lengths that develop over the scope of aspect ratios evident in Figure 12a. While this discussion has focused on cracking, this gap also develops regarding some forms of areal corrosion / metal-loss.

The second compatibility gap develops in regard to the complex nature of the cracking produced by some cracking mechanisms, which also can be evident for corrosion. Such complexity is apparent in the appearance of the features on the surface of the pipeline (e.g., SCC), but also can be evident on the plane they grow on through-wall (e.g., hook crack). Such complexity is not a factor in Level 1 models, because it is beyond what can be viably characterized at that level, nor is it an issue for Level 3 approaches, because it could be modelled at that level. However, it would be an issue for Level 2 criteria, without which such complexity could not be bundled into the technology that might be carried on an ILI platform. Complexity exists for interaction between features separated by the local wall thickness, as well as for coalescence between adjacent features within an area bounded by the local wall thickness.

The third compatibility gap develops in view of the observation that local properties control failure, which can only be addressed in the IM process if the inspection supports viable spatial resolution and viable feature ID. As has been illustrated in contrasting the failure boundaries in Figure 6, significant differences in the outcome of the IM can result from the spread of toughness levels considered therein. Given the different resistances evident in Figures 5a and 5b, depending on the operating temperature a four-fold swing in toughness can occur between adjacent joints of pipe, which in turn might drive quite different IM decisions. Uncertain local toughness inputs to any Level of predictive model thus are a major gap. If a worst-case resistance must be used in the FFS analysis because the ILI lacks spatial resolution, the outcome could lead to expensive maintenance with marginal risk reduction. While some Vendors are working on technology to quantify the mechanical properties, the ability to quantify local resistance in terms of the UTS seems a long way off, with toughness much less local toughness still more distant.

Closure

Are we measuring and managing the wrong traits?

Threat identification and assessment is central to codified assessment procedures like ASME B31.8S, and other comparable schemes. B31.8S further notes that all threats to pipeline integrity shall be considered. The term "threat" is then associated with the 22[*] direct cause categories as classified by the PRCI[76] in work motivated by INGAA. Threats in this context include 'direct causes' such as corrosion, SCC, material and construction defects, equipment failure, damage, and so on. But these measures of integrity are consequences of poor management, maintenance, and bad decisions rather than direct causes or root causes of the resulting degradation.

Reality is that the just-noted consequences are avoided by managing the factors that affect their causes. Success measured in terms of incident frequency, as in Figure 3, does not reflect trends in their causative factors. In this regard, the public's or media's success metrics don't contribute to understanding how IM is altering the likelihood of

---

[*] This result was specific to the analysis of NG transmission pipelines from 1985 through 1997.

incidents. One could reasonably ask in this context – are we monitoring the wrong metrics or managing the wrong traits? For example, external corrosion has many controlling factors or drivers. For pipelines these drivers are slowed by a coating, and a cathodic protection (CP) system. As long as the coating and the CP are correctly selected / designed, and functioning as intended, in theory all is well. At a high level, monitoring at rectifiers integrates the conditions along that segment, whereas locally unknown or ill-understood degradation may be active. It could reflect local groundwater and/or soil, or it could be due to local interference, various bio drivers, and/or other local factors. Field-proven aboveground survey tools exist to characterize line location, coating condition, and burial depth, with direct-assessment practices codified to locate "hotspots" – which taken together and aligned define one of the layers that needs to be integrated into leading practices like risk-management models. But, not all Operators develop such practices and/or deploy such tools.

Three questions that beg answers

Three questions beg answers in view of the diminishing returns and the other observations made throughout the above discussion:

1. Is the current inspection-based IM concept flawed?
2. If the approach is not flawed, do gaps such as those noted confound its implementation? How should the stakeholders best organize to bridge the gaps noted, and what is the minimum framework and related criteria to affect a continuing reduction in incident frequency using this approach?
3. Do metrics that reflect high-level consequences (i.e., the threats) contain sufficient detail to assure the integrity of an aging non-redundant infrastructure?

The answer to #1 follows by reference to other successful applications of this concept, in other industries like aerospace, which like pipelines are transportation systems that experience very occasional high-consequence events. Track records suggest the concept can be viable. Analysis of implementation gaps has shown a strong influence on the failure response of a pipeline, but whether their resolution would affect a step change in incident rate needs to be quantified along with the role of the metrics. Until these aspects get quantified, I contend that continuing on the same path will not offset the diminishing returns from today's practices, and that maintaining the current level will cost more to achieve in the future – without a clear benefit either as reduced risk to the public and environment, and/or reduced incident rate.

What could be changed near-term, and how?

Many aspects might be listed under such a heading whose inclusion depends on 1) how well defined and/or quantified the issues are, 2) the scope of such concerns, and 3) the impact on IM to offset the diminishing returns. If the scope is limited, or if the issues are well defined and prioritized in regard to safety, and a clear path exists to resolve them, then a R&D program can be developed to manage them. In contrast, if the scope is broad, and/or the issues are ill defined, and their IM impact has not been quantified, then their practical significance for safety and risk management is unclear and cannot be prioritized.

Quantify the IM significance of the gaps as the basis to prioritize

The above discussion identified nine gaps, and quantified the significance of one aspect of the broader compatibility gap between the outputs of inspection and the required inputs for condition-based IM. While the associated error in the wall stress at failure in some instances was about 10% of SMYS, which is significant in regard to pipe burst, it might be of lesser significance if impending failure is controlled by fatigue, for example. Thus, this element requires further evaluation before its significance can be assessed more broadly, and the need for its resolution prioritized. The same can be said in regard to all gaps noted, which exist among others, and remain ill-quantified ~20 years after condition-based IM was codified. Initiating analyses to prioritize the IM impact of such gaps should help to counter the diminishing returns trend evident between Figures 2a and 3, and so would be a step improvement in the IM process. Success metrics should include historic parameters like incident and catastrophic event frequencies, with a refined monetized set developed and tracked by the operators to determine if their IM procedures are effectively managing their incidents.

While nine important gaps have been identified and some aspects quantified relative to their IM implications, the gaps considered are but a few among others that could not be addressed in this Chapter, which is already too long. Reflecting on the above-noted gaps and those not addressed, suffice it to note that by the year 2000 the OIG[27] had both recognized and reported that inspection tools were inadequate to establishing pipeline condition. While some successes can be claimed as a result of the PHMSA's investments and collaboration with the industry and its Vendors to improve the capabilities of 'smart pigs' and the IM process, the Public's metric as quantified in Figure 3 shows no net gain.

Respond consistently to research and development (R&D) needs

Periodically the PHMSA holds Forums to identify and prioritize R&D needs, but at times their process appears subjective, perhaps motivated by a hidden agenda. The outcomes of a given working group (WG) can often be determined or influenced strongly by the interests – and so the mix – of the 25 or so individuals present in a WG. Occasionally, highly ranked needs are absent in the ensuing Research Announcement (RA). For example, the WG that considered 'Expanding ILI Capabilities and Applications' in the 2018 forum voted 'an in-line-based means to quantify local toughness' second among their top three needs. Yet the RA that appeared early in 2019 does not mention toughness, much less seek work to address this need. This seems puzzling given that the first-to-fail balance between collapse and fracture tips strongly toward fracture in lower-toughness scenarios, such as ERW seams. Regardless of how difficult it might be to address toughness, the fact remains that related failures will occur until this highly-ranked need gets addressed. Funding studies to marginalize it or deciding to ignore it will not avoid the next Mayflower incident: but they will open to the Public backlash that ensues.

Since the focus on damage prevention has affected a downward trend in such failures, collapse-controlled-controlled failures due for example to corrosion have been the most common cause of incidents. In contrast, fracture-controlled failures that often split the pipe, causing a major release, drive the catastrophic event frequency. While infrequent, catastrophic events get the media (social and news) coverage and scrutiny, and fuel the public's pushback regarding pipelines. For such reasons, the available resources have to be balanced across a range of concerns, with such work done under funding that in terms of net dollars for the R&D has been roughly level for some time. Resolving this leads to the next suggested short-term change.

Change the funding and prioritization processes and the management metrics

Based on the above, the funding must expand to first quantitatively prioritize and then focus on the R&D that bridges the high-value gaps, where value is quantified by its impact on IM, free of individual or corporate bias / interests. Proposals should present a clear rational low-risk staged-gate technical path, in enough detail that quantitative success metrics can be defined as the basis to progress to the next gate. The Industry and the Government then need to align to deliver integrated solutions – with each targeting aspects that are focused on their metrics and aligned with the Public's primary measure – which is a reduction in catastrophic events and the overall incident rate. Metrics touted by the PHMSA since 2002 have yet to include this essential outcome.

Current PHMSA metrics that consider patents applied for, commercialization of technology, and reports and papers published reflect R&D rather than drivers to reduce incident rate. Until R&D affects a marked reduction in incident rate it lacks value in light of the Public's success metrics. While "over 21 million website visits since 2002, with over 1.5 million downloads since 2008"[77] might reflect the R&D's significance, it equally could reflect study of that R&D to identify gaps, and the need for further research. While the payoff from R&D has a time horizon, at some point it has to show value as reduced incident rate. Unfortunately, Figure 3 shows this rate has not declined since 2002, which suggests website hits and downloads likely reflect the study of the past R&D to find gaps, and in turn perpetuate R&D rather than delivering a reduced incident rate. Changes are needed in the value metrics to reflect drivers that reduce incident rate.

References

1. Woodley, D., "The Origin of Intelligent Pigs," Pipelines International, December 2011, pp. 26-30.

2. Leis, B. N., "Review of Response Requirements and Criteria for Plain Dents," PRCI Project MD-4-13 Report, PR-214-163713-R01, July, 2018.

3. Drake, A. J., in testimony on behalf of INGAA to the NTSB, NTSB Public Hearing on Pipeline Safety, Washington, DC, November 2000.

4. Grover, J., "Advances in Pipeline Inspection Technologies," GE-PII paper PetroMin Gas Pipeline Conference, 2002.

5. Anon., "Fitness-for-Service," API Recommended Practice 579, 2000: (A second edition was published in 2007 joint with "ASME FFS-1 2007" being issued as "579-1 / ASME FFS-1 2007.")

6. Anon., "Manual for Determining the Remaining Strength of Corroded Pipelines," B31G ANSI/ASME,1984. (this document has been updated and rereleased several times)

7. Kiefner, J. F. and Vieth, P. H., "A Modified Criterion for Evaluating the Remaining Strength of Corroded Pipe," Final Report on Project PR 3-805 to the PRC of the AGA, December 22, 1989.

8. Vieth, P. H. and Kiefner, J. F., "RSTRENG User's Manual and Software," AGA Catalog No. L51688 and L51688A, March 1993: see also Kiefner, J. F., Vieth, P. H., and Roytman, I., "Continuing Validation of RSTRENG," Pipeline Research Supervisory Committee, AGA Catalog No. L51689, 1996.

9. Leis, B.N. and Stephens, D.R., An Alternative Approach to Assess the Integrity of Corroded Line Pipe – Part I: Current status, Paper No. ISOPE-I-97-490; Part II: Alternative criterion, Paper No. ISOPE-I-97-491, Seventh International Offshore and Polar Engineering Conference, Honolulu, May 1997, pp. 624-634 and 635-641.

10. Jaske, C. E., 1996, "CorLAS™ 1.0 User Manual: Computer Program for Corrosion-Life Assessment of Piping and Pressure Vessels," Version 1.0, CC Technologies Systems, Inc., Dublin, OH, 1996: "Addendum to User Manual for Version 2.0 of CorLAS™," CC Technologies Systems Inc., Dublin, OH, 1999.

11. Fu, B., Stephens, D., Ritchie, D., and Jones, C. L., "Methods for Assessing Corroded Pipelines – Review, Validation, and Recommendations," BG Technology Limited, GRTC R3281, Restricted to PRCI members and distribution list, PRCI Cat. No. L51878, August 2000.

12. Kiefner, J. F., Maxey, W. A., and Eiber, R. J., "A Study of the Causes of Failure of Defects That Have Survived a Prior Hydrostatic Test," PRC - American Gas Association, NG-18 Report No. 111, November 1980.

13. Leis, B.N., Brust, F.W. and Scott, P.M., 1991. Development and Validation of a Ductile Flaw Growth Analysis for Gas Transmission Line Pipe. NG-18 Report No. 193. Catalogue No. L51643, PRCI.

14. Leis, B.N. and Eiber, R.J., "Fracture Control Technology for Transmission Pipelines," Project Nos. PR-003-00108 and PR-003-084506, Member-Only Availability, PRCI, 2015

15. Leis, B. N., Rudland, D. L., and Eiber, R. J., "Evaluation of the Benefits of Hydrotesting Gas-transmission Pipelines," PR 3-9523, PRCI, Catalog No. L51844e, February 1997.

16. Leis, B. N. and Verley, R., "Quality Control, NDT Offer Alternatives to Hydrotesting," *Pipe Line & Gas Journal*, Vol. 83, August, 2000, pp. 31-34.

17. Anon., "Submarine pipeline systems," DNV-OS-F101, (edition published in 2000)

18. Anon., "Managing System Integrity for Hazardous Liquid Pipelines," API 1160, 2nd Edition, 2013. (The first release of this document is dated November 2001)

19. Anon., "Managing System Integrity of Gas Pipelines," ASME B31.8S, 2016. (first release 31 January 2002).

20. Anon., "Accountable Pipeline Safety and Partnership Act of 1996," Public Law 104–304, 104th Congress, S 1505, 1996.

21. Anon., "Beyond Compliance: Creating a Responsible Regulatory Environment that Promotes Excellence, Innovation, and Efficiency; A Progress Report on the Pipeline Risk Management Demonstration Program," OPS / API / INGAA, May 1999.

22. Anon., Annex J in "CSA Z662-15, Oil and Gas Pipeline Systems," Canadian Standards Association, 2015.

23. Anon., "Pipeline Safety NOPR: Pipeline Integrity Management in High Consequence Areas (Hazardous Liquid Operators with Less Than 500 Miles of Pipeline)," 66 Federal Registry, p. 15,821, 21 March 2001.

24. Anon., "Pipeline Safety NOPR: Pipeline Integrity Management in High Consequence Areas (Gas Transmission Pipelines), 68 Federal Registry, p. 4,278, 28 January 2003.

25. Coyner, K, p 104 of Senate Hearing 106-1114 concerning the Reauthorization of the Pipeline Safety Act by then head of the Research and Special Programs Administration, May 2000.

26. Scheinberg, P. F. and Ratzenberger, J., "The Office of Pipeline Safety Is Changing How It Oversees the Pipeline Industry" General Accounting Office Report to the House of Representatives, GAO/RCED-00-128, May 2000.

27. Mead, K. M., Testimony before the US Senate by the Inspector General concerning the "Reauthorization of the Pipeline Safety Program," Report No. RT-2000-092, May 2000

28. Anon., "Rupture of Hazardous Liquid Pipeline with Release and Ignition of Propane, Carmichael, Mississippi, November 1 2007," NTSB PAR-09/01, October 2009.

29. Zakar, F. P., "Materials Laboratory Factual Report Draft" NTSB No. DCA08MP001, Rod Dyck, Investigator, NTSB Report No.07-122, 18 April 2008. (Marked 'To be used only within Parties of Investigation')

30. Kiefner J. F., Haines, H., Rosenfeld, M., Beavers, J. A., Amend, B., Bruce, W. A., Leis, B. N., Zhu, X-K., Nestleroth, J. B., and Clark, E., "Gap Analysis and Review of NTSB Report PAR 09-01," PRCI Report No. PR-218-103706, 21 January 2011.

31. Hersman, D. A. P., "NTSB Recommendations P-09-1 through -3" Correspondence to Cynthia Douglass, Acting Deputy Administrator, PHMSA, October 27 2009.

32. Leis, B. N. and Cosham, A., "Flap Pressure and Arrest Length Considerations in Propagating Shear Failure," J of Pipeline Engineering, Vol, 15, No. 4, pp. 231-242, 2016.

33. Leis, B. N., Young, B. A., Kiefner, J. F., Nestleroth, J. B., Beavers, J. A., Quickel, G. T., and Brossia, C. S. "Final Summary Report and Recommendations for the Comprehensive Study to Understand Longitudinal ERW Seam Failures – Phase One," Contract No. DTPH56-11-T-000003, October 2013.

34. Young, B. A., Olson, R. J., and O'Brian, J. M., "Final Report for Phase II of the Comprehensive Study to Understand Longitudinal ERW Seam Failures," Contract No. DTPH56-11-T-000003, August 2017.

35. Anon., "List of Pipeline Accidents in the United States," Last accessed 03/27/2019, https://en.wikipedia.org/wiki/Category:Lists_of_pipeline_accidents_in_the_United_States

36. Anon., "List of Pipeline Accidents in the United States in 2000," Last accessed 03/27/2019, https://en.wikipedia.org/wiki/List_of_pipeline_accidents_in_the_United_States_in_2000.

37. Anon., "List of Pipeline Accidents in the United States in the 21st century," last accessed 2/16/2019, http://en.wikipedia.org/wiki/List_of_pipeline_accidents_in_the_United_States in_the_21st_century

38. Kiefner J. F., Kolovich, K.M., Macrory-Dalton, C. J., Johnston, D.C., Maier, C.J., and Beavers, J. A., "Track Record of In-Line Inspection as a Means of ERW Seam Integrity Assessment," Contract No. DTPH56-11-T-000003, November 2012.

39. Leis, B. N., "Compare - Contrast Analysis of Inspection Data and Failure Predictions versus Burst-Test Outcomes for ERW-Seam Defects," Contract No. DTPH56-11-T-000003, June 2013.

40. Anon., "Texas Eastern Transmission Corporation Natural Gas Pipeline Explosion and Fire, Edison New Jersey, March 23, 1994," NTSB PAR•95/01, 18 January 1995.

41. Anon., Addendum (Reconsideration Request) for PAR-95-01, PB95-916501, 18 May 2001.

42. Anon., "Failure Investigation Report: Plains Pipeline, LP, Line 901 Crude Oil Release," May 19, 2015, Santa Barbara County, California, May 2016.

43. Anon., "Pipeline Rupture and Subsequent Fire in Bellingham, Washington, June 10, 1999," NTSB/PAR-02/02, October 2001

44. Anon., "Rupture of Piney Point Oil Pipeline and Release of Fuel Oil Near Chalk Point, Maryland, April 7, 2000," NTSB/PAR-02/01, July 2002.

45. Anon., "Colonial Pipeline Company Petroleum Product Leak, Centreville, Virginia." NTSB/PAB-17/01, June 2017.

46. Zhu, X. K., Leis, B. N., and Clark, E. B., "Integrity Management for Wrinklebends and Buckles," PHMSA Contract No. DTRS56-05-T-0003, December 2007.

47. Anon., "Goal is Zero Incidents," http://www.ingaa.org/6211/11460.aspx, last accessed August 2011.

48. Leis, B N., McSweeney, T. I., Nestleroth, J. B., Clark, E. B., and Sanzone, D. M. "Keystone XL Pipeline: Independent Engineering Assessment – Final Report to TransCanada Pipelines Ltd.," December 2013. (marked Privileged and Confidential) https://keystonepipeline-xl.state.gov/documents/organization/221277.pdf

49. Anon., "PHMSA Raw Data Files," https://www.phmsa.dot.gov/data-and-statistics/pipeline/gas-distribution-gas-gathering-gas-transmission-hazardous-liquids; see also https://primis.phmsa.dot.gov/comm/reports/safety/docs/IncidentReportingCriteriaHistory1990-2011.pdf

50. Hogfoss, R. and Little, C., (representing Hunton and Williams LLP) "Release Reporting Issues and Developments," AOPL Business Conference: Roundtable Topic 5, September 2013, www.pipelinelaw.com

51. Kiefner, J. F. and Trench, C. J., "Oil Pipeline Characteristics and Risk Factors: Illustrations from the Decade of Construction," API, December 2001.

52. Clark, E. B., Leis, B. N., and Eiber, R. J., "Integrity of Vintage Pipelines," Final Report to the INGAA Foundation, Battelle, October 2004.

53. Duffy, A. R., McClure, G. M., Maxey, W. A. and Atterbury, T. J., "Study of the Feasibility of Basing Natural Gas Pipeline Operating Pressure on Hydrostatic Test Pressure," Catalogue No. L30050, AGA, 1968.

54. Leis, B.N., "Managing an Aging Pipeline Infrastructure," Chapter 44 in Oil and Gas Pipelines: Integrity and Safety Handbook, R. W. Revie, Editor., Wiley, 2014, pp 609-633.

55. Leis, B. N., "Pipelines Past and Present – But what Does the Future Hold? Keynote Address, Proceedings of Technology for Future and Ageing Pipelines, Gent, Great Southern Press, April 2018, pp. 3-23

56. Anon., "List of pipeline accidents (for the World)," Last accessed 03/27/2019, https://en.wikipedia.org/w/index.php?title=List_of_pipeline_accidents&oldid=887186179

57. Anon., "Energy Pipeline Research, Development, and Demonstration Act of 2002," Public Law 107-355, HR 3929, 107th Congress, 2002.

58. Anon., "PHMSA 20 Year Trends," Last accessed 03/27/2019, https://www.phmsa.dot.gov/data-and-statistics/pipeline/pipeline-incident-20-year-trends

59. Keener, B., "Incident Report Criteria History," 27 May 2014. Last accessed 04/23/2019 https://www.phmsa.dot.gov/sites/phmsa.dot.gov/files/docs/pdmpublic_incident_page_allrpt.pdf

60. Leis, B.N., "Material and Construction Defects," Chapter 11 in ***Managing Pipeline Threats***, Clarion, J. Tiratsoo, Ed., 2020.

61. Stonesifer, R. B., Brust, F. W., and Leis, B. N., "Mixed Mode Stress Intensity Factors for Interacting Semi-Elliptical Surface Cracks in a Plate," *Eng Fracture Mech*, Vol. 45, No. 3, 1993, pp. 357-380.

62. Leis, B. N., "Characterization of Axial Flaws in Pipelines, With a Focus on Stress-Corrosion Cracking: NG-18 Report No. 212, PRCI, 1995.

63. Anon., "Public Inquiry Concerning Stress Corrosion Cracking on Canadian Oil and Gas Pipelines," by Canadian National Energy Board, November, 1996, p. 137.

64. Rothwell, A., B., and Coote, R. I., "A Critical Review of Assessment Methods for Axial Planar Surface Flaws in Pipe," Paper 52, Proceedings ***Pipeline Technology Conference***, Ostend, October 2009.

65. Kiefner, J. F. and Kolovitch, K. M., "Models for Predicting Failure Stress Levels for Defects Affecting ERW and Flash-Welded Seams; with an addendum by Brian Leis presenting Battelle's experience with the PAFFC model," KAI Interim Report on Task 2.4, US DoT Contract No. DTPH56-11-T-000003, January 2013.

66. Leis, B. N., "Characterizing the Fracture Resistance of ERW Seams," *J. of Pipeline Engr*, Q3 2018, pp. 165-181.
67. Anon., "It's all about the Data," TDW Brochure, 2012. (last accessed 04/28/2016: now at http://www.texasgas.com/wp-content/uploads/2017/11/Microsoft-PowerPoint-TGA-Transmission-Roundtable-Its-all-about-the-data-Rev1-Read-Only.pdf.
68. Anon., "Specifications and Requirements for Intelligent Pig Inspection of Pipelines," Pipeline Operators Forum, April, 1996. (first release renamed "Specifications and requirements for in-line inspection of pipelines" since, and as of 2019 was in its fifth release.
69. Anon., Guidance on Field Verification Procedures for In-Line-Inspection, POF, December 2012.
70. Anon., "In-Line Inspection of Pipelines," NACE SP0102 (formerly RP0102), NACE International, 2017.
71. Anon., "Get to Know your Pipeline Better," Linalog Brochure, AMF Tuboscope, Inc. Form #945, October, 1984.
72. Gao, M., "Mechanical Damage in Pipelines: A Review of the Methods and Improvements in Characterization, Evaluation, and Mitigation," Chapter 44 in ***Oil and Gas Pipelines: Integrity and Safety Handbook***, R. W. Revie, Editor, Wiley, 2014, pp 609-633.
73. Huyse, L., Monroe, J., and van Roodselaar, A., "Effects of In-Line Inspection Sizing Uncertainties on In-The-Ditch Validation: Review of Results," Rio Pipeline Conference, Rio de Janeiro, September 2011, IBP1185-11.
74. McNealy, R., "Effective Integrity Management Incorporates Tool Performance," *Oil and Gas J.*, 04/17/2006
75. Parkins, R. N., Leis, B. N., and Christman, T. K., "Spatial Density of Stress-Corrosion Cracks in Line-Pipe Steels," NG-18 Report No. 195, Pipeline Research Committee International, April 1992.
76. Kiefner, J. F., Mesloh, R. E., and Kiefner, B. A., "Analysis of DOT Reportable Incidents for Gas Transmission Pipelines and Gathering Systems," PRCI Contract #218-9801, January 2000.
77. Anon., Pipeline Safety Research and Development Announcement Details, Research Announcement #693JK3191RA01, PHMSA, February, 2018.

Is there a lack of thought/ competence in pipeline welding practices?

Dr. Keith Leewis

> *Welding technology always changes over time and standards are somewhat slow to be upgraded. I'd encourage the welding engineer to think out the whole problem without just using rote technology requirements from lagging standards that were written for an earlier and quite different steel metallurgy.*

How did I get here?

Back in 1967 I knew I didn't want to work a manual job after high school, so I applied to several universities and surprise I was accepted into more than one engineering school. Metallurgy seemed to offer answers to how the world went around and McMaster had just built a new Engineering Building and had a nuclear reactor too. Off I went and learned how to adjust to hard work and various joys and disappointments, such as helping run the engineering society and learning to play a mean bridge rubber instead of doing homework. This garnered a spring invitation to the Dean's tea party. Since I had earned one "A" and failed by only 2%, I was permitted to repeat the year. This was great, since the alternative was to be asked to never darken the Engineering School doorway again. By the end of second-year, only about 30% of those lads (and very few lasses) that started on day one were still enrolled. Failure killed my grade average over my four plus one years as an undergraduate: therefore, no grad school, it was off to work. I still believe that an average student can graduate from engineering if they are willing to concentrate and do the work.

Sad to say every time I graduated it seemed that there was another recession, leaving limited new vocational choices. They turned out to be good choices, just few. My first job was learning to turn coal, limestone, and iron ore into rolled steel products. My employer had a great introductory program for new engineers that required three-month rotations in the different departments to learn to appreciate the various people, work areas, and challenges. I had a chance to work in steelmaking, hot and cold rolling, and electrolytic sheet galvanization. After a year, engineers such as me were offered a job in one of these areas.

When the job appeared, I chose to work in the R&D department and went on to help design and install the new desulphurization technology, which was needed to manage the blast furnace problem of alkali constipation. Essentially a leaner slag composition was needed to remove these sodium and potassium compounds. If not removed, these compounds would condense and solidify part way up the furnace interior, gluing the feed together, blocking the flow of gas up, ore, limestone, and coke down into the lower, mostly liquid part of the furnace. This leaner slag meant the liquid iron sulphur was too high for steel making and had to be removed before the liquid iron was poured into the basic oxygen steel furnace (BOF) to begin steelmaking. We started desulphurization treatments, first plunging magnesium into the hot metal transfer rail car and then replacing that technique with a dedicated powdered calcium carbide injection lance.

After five years, grad school beckoned and I received an educational leave of absence. Two earlier years of MBA night school taught me two things; one I wanted to stick to engineering, not business, and two, full time day school was the best way. I was accepted as a mature student on probation, so I asked my wife to go back to work, now as the primary wage earner, and take care of our new baby, while I went back to "Skule" by cashing in my fledgling retirement saving plan for the tuition and expenses. We are still married, now almost 50 years.

My masters at the University of Toronto focused on the kinetics of ladle metallurgy processes. If you remember in 1972, the Arabs shut off the oil and energy costs shot through the roof. Steel making had to change. Ingot casting was too inefficient and continuous casting was the savior, but all the steel conditioning and processing after the furnace had to change. Alloying was still done in the steel ladle, but the denitrogenization, deoxidation, and desulphurization processes all had to be refined in the ladle to precondition the steel prior to adding rare earths and other austenitic precipitate forming alloys prior to solidification. We helped develop the furnace slag controls, plus refined the alloy injections by bags of, bullets of, or wire feeding of aluminum, rare earths, calcium and magnesium metals that caused the dissolved tramp elements to precipitate and thus ensured shape control of the oxy-sulphides. We improved the argon stirring process to help purge nitrogen and carbon dioxide and aid thermal and microalloy homogenization.

I was fortunate to continue studying gas-slag-liquid steel equilibrium and kinetics for my PhD. On graduation from the Technical University of Nova Scotia, my steel company was laying off employees including me; however, I was assured that I could return. I was therefore very pleased to accept an assistant professorship. Rather than steelmaking, I started a graduate program on welding; adapting from 300-ton heats to 3-gram puddles. I began a small Canadian welding research program in alloying for weld strength and toughness for the excavators in the tar sands, ice breakers, and Navy submarines. It took me five years and many publications to be promoted to associate as a tenured professor.

My interest in welding had strengthened and I left the university community to become the Director of Technology at the Welding Institute of Canada. At WIC, I inherited the steel pipeline construction, fracture mechanics, and repair programs, as well as new multi-feed welding machines plus providing technical support for the pipelines, automotive, and rail industries. Plus, there was a five-year practical period as a welding engineer, senior metallurgist and co-developer of the original risk assessment program for TransCanada pipelines before joining the Gas Research Institute. Once there, I helped manage a wide range of integrity-related processes to inspect for and then address all the pipeline integrity threats. I also managed construction and repair technologies in these pipeline research programs, including those at the Pipeline Research Council International, before becoming a consultant to the natural gas pipeline industry.

Introduction

Often, I come across folks that don't necessarily think out the whole problem and just want to speed up a welding process or use rote technology requirements from standards that were written for an earlier and different steel metallurgy. Technology always changes over time and standards are somewhat slow to be upgraded, especially if the subject matter experts are in a different field of expertise and unaware of these changes. That causes problems. Too often, we become aware only after we have killed or maimed a fellow employee or contractor.

My career bridged the industry change-over from the earlier ingot solidification of pearlitic steels to the modern continuous casting of microalloyed steels. These changes were forced during the 1970s when energy costs increased and the older ways of doing business were too inefficient to continue. Modern and older steels are similar and are still described as one, but they are not alike. Steels are compositionally not much different, but modern steels get their strength in very different ways. They behave very differently when subjected to high-temperature thermal cycling. Think about what is expected to change when faced with modern materials.

Example 1: A good example of "think about what you are doing" arose in a hydrotesting problem around 2012. The pipeline operator was building a new pipeline to run at 80% specified minimum yield strength (SMYS). They bought pipe from a new steel mill that had just learned to make X70 pipe. The Material Transfer Records (MTRs) showed that all the steel tested correctly, and all the selected joints exceeded SMYS. The post-construction hydrotest was passed. The caliper tool was run a month or so after start-up, and they discovered many 0.25 to 2% bulges or "outie dents." Where did they come from?

Looking back at the MTRs, the yield distribution and statistics showed the average at 107% SMYS, but had a coefficient of variation (COV) of over 4%, indicating poor process control causing a significant number of joints (about 1%) in the new pipeline to have yields less than SMYS. The construction test pressure was SMYS at the top-of-the-hill and higher in the valley and those outie bulges were the result. The regulator made them replace everyone over 0.5%. Ouch!

Unfortunately, there were no white beards around who remembered that there was a similar problem back in the 1970s when steel makers were learning to make pipe from continuously cast steel rather than ingots. Some pipe joints after the hydrotest were bulging even at a lower test pressure of 125% MAOP or 90% SMYS. The original problem was a lack of mill process control. In those days, the hydrotesting protocols were improved to also track the volume of water injected while the pipe was being pressurized. Engineers should have ensured that the internal volume plus 0.2% was not exceeded. Unfortunately, following the test there was no evaluation to determine what was happening.

ASME B31.8 Appendix N describes pressure testing. Most folks have long used ASME B31.8 Appendix N-5 (c1) and filled until the pressure rise requires twice as many pump strokes. They have forgotten that (c2) specifically cautions against exceeding 0.2% of the internal pipe volume. This is what happened in example 1. They kept filling using the simple rule while the pipe kept yielding and bulging and the crew didn't stop until twice as many strokes were needed for the same pressure rise. Nothing like reinventing the wheel!

Most of the standards are written to assume common materials, but materials improve and change. We need to be vigilant and ensure we are dealing with apples and apples. Unfortunately, we are dealt oranges from time to time.

Example 2: Forged fittings used to be pearlitic grades of alloy steel, but more and more manufacturers are forced to buy and forge microalloy steel plate. The strength of microalloyed steel is metastable due to the high dislocation density and quenched very fine microstructures (metallurgical descriptions follow). All fittings are much thicker than pipe and are dimensioned after castings. Castings, however, still tend to be pearlitic steels with higher carbon and alloy contents for adding strength. These castings have wall thicknesses more than twice that of the pipe because of their coarse solidification structure, unlike plate which is a finer rolled microstructure. These pearlitic steel castings require post weld heat treatment to minimize stress risers and allow hydrogen diffusion.

Pearlitic steels fortunately tend to strengthen after thermal cycling. This historical thermocycle program for post weld heat treatment does not work for fittings made from microalloyed plate. The properties of microalloyed fittings are metastable and these fittings get much weaker if you heat them. Both the Canadian and U.S. regulators have issued warnings about these problems, and PRCI has publications to help avoid these modern fitting problems. These fittings were all cut-outs too.

Today you can only buy a modern microalloyed steels for saddles or a type A & B steel sleeves to reinforce/repair old pearlitic carrier pipe. The welding engineer still needs to ensure the welding procedure is correct for the two different steels. The correct procedure will minimize strains and avoid hydrogen cracking. The temptation is to use a large weld puddle to quickly complete the job. The high heat input will weaken the sleeve, while the large weld volume will increase the strains and increase the chance for hydrogen cracking. The proven procedure takes longer and uses many small heat input weld passes sequenced to strain relieve the previous pass and allow time for hydrogen diffusion. The lower heat inputs cause a lower thermal cycle and will also help preserve the strength in the sleeve heat affected zone (HAZ).

Compressor stations use heavy wall pipe and heavier wall fittings. Again, choose small weld puddle, narrow gap welding processes to minimize the HAZ softening and avoid post-weld heat treatments that can weaken the pipe and fitting (unless older technology pearlitic castings and pearlitic pipe are used). Now can you can see why it is important to develop or confirm that the welding procedure you are using remains correct for the job.

Steelmaking in my lifetime

PHMSA records indicate that about 70% of the steel pipe in service today in the USA was made from pearlitic steels. After World War II, some steels were still being made in acid open-hearth furnaces. But the 1950s and 1960s saw a great conversion to basic oxygen furnaces (BOF). In these furnaces the oxygen was blown down a water-cooled lance to burn and remove carbon, silicon, and manganese from the blast furnace liquid-iron and make steel. When the carbon was reduced to about 0.25%, the oxygen flow was stopped, and the steel heat was ready for the next step.

The steel was then poured into acid lined ladles keeping most of the slag back while silicon for deoxidation and manganese for Sulphur control was mostly added in bulk until the analysis from the furnace samples came back and trim additions were then added by hand. The BOF basic slag was retained in the furnace to minimize the transfer of unwanted elements and prevent it from dissolving the acid refractories lining the transfer or teeming ladle used to meter the liquid steel into the ingots. Later on, "ladle metallurgy" processes would require a basic refractory lining.

The teeming ladle was carried by crane to the teeming floor for casting. The steel was metered through a drain hole in the base of the ladle using a stopper-rod mechanism. The steel was poured into tapered rectangular cast iron "ingot molds" sitting on flat cast iron "stools." As the steel cooled, the liquid boiled or effervesced as the nitrogen and oxygen evolved as CO bubbles. These "rimming" steels had very low alloy content on the exterior of the solidified ingot and produced better rolled surfaces.

Refractory sideboards were used at the top of the ingots to slow solidification and allow the last liquid to fill the central pipe as solidification reduced the volume. Oxygen removal was sometimes handled by aluminum additions to the ladle, where the inclusions could float and get trapped in the ladle slag. Aluminum was added into the ladles to minimize the rimming action and ensure the steel was "killed" or had little gas evolution. Trim aluminum was also added into the ingots to kill any rimming, but these aluminum oxides were trapped by the iron dendrites during solidification and became inclusions.

The solid ingots were pushed out of their cast iron molds and conveyed to the soaking pits in the hot mill. In the soaking pit they were reheated to white heat and then slabbed, generally in a 2-hi mill, and while still orange hot, were multi-stand rolled into coils or plates and then cooled. Only about ¾ of the steel ingot weight made it out the door as plate or coiled steel, and the rest was recycled as heavy scrap. The top of each ingot was cropped to remove the biggest inclusions, and these end cuts and other heavy mill scrap steel were re-melted in the BOF, sometimes much as 30% of the total charge weight. Not an efficient use of energy and materials.

Ingot casting thus became too energy expensive after the oil crisis in the early 1970s. As a result, mills began to convert from using ingots for solidification to using continuous casters. This endless solidification process allowed the steel to solidify in a bottomless, water-cooled copper rectangle. The steel would emerge as a slab, be cut to length, and go straight through into the multi-stand rolling mill with minimal reheating and minimal scrap generation. The energy and steel efficiency improved greatly.

Also, during the 1970s, there was a strong push to increase the grade of steel used for pipelines from X52/X60 to X70/X80. A higher grade of steel allowed thinner wall pipe, resulting in fewer weld passes needed to complete a girth weld. A thinner wall also results in lighter pipe, lower purchase cost, and easier transportation logistics. In addition, costs are reduced for moving pipe over difficult and remote terrain such as in Alaska and the Arctic. Finally, fewer weld passes per joint also suggested the production rate could be raised and more miles per day of production were possible.

Strength comes from microstructure

The formation of iron carbide is a well-understood phenomenon described in the nose-shaped time temperature transformation (TTT) diagram or the continuous cooling transformation (CCT) diagram. The iron carbide precipitates as the steel cools from the higher temperature austenitic phase (where carbon is in solution), to the lower temperature ferritic phase (where the carbon precipitates as an iron carbide). If the cooling rate is fast enough, then the path does not go through the nose of the TTT/CCT diagram, and bainite or even martensite structures are the result.

When the steel is hot-rolled, the dislocation density helps the formation of new grains on the old austenitic grain boundaries. Grains grow consuming the smaller adjacent grains. If the grain boundaries can be pinned (held in place) by small microalloy inclusions, then the many small grains can't grow and remain restrained and small. On every rolling pass there are even more dislocations to intersect with grain boundaries and re-nucleate even finer sized austenitic grains. This is especially evident if the last pass happens very low in the austenite phase field. Here, finer austenite grains nucleate even finer pearlitic, bainite or even martensite structures. It is the fine structure that provides the strength by making dislocation movement difficult. This increase in strength and loss in ductility is achieved as the fine metastable structure is trapped until heating causes it to deteriorate.

Older Pearlitic steels have a cooling rate designed to cross through the nose of the CCT diagram so that 100% of the carbon becomes a parallel lamella structure of fine iron carbonate and ferrite known as pearlite. The pearlite structure interrupts dislocation shear, providing the strength mechanism for the steel. The big advantage of pearlite is the response to a following thermal cycle. The reheated steel usually cools at the same or faster rate so that the lamella become even finer, and the strength improves. This means that forcing the steel through a heating thermal cycle tends to improve the strength of the joint. This proves helpful in welding pearlitic steels.

Pearlitic steels depend on fine iron carbide lamella inside a smaller grain ferrite annealed steel structure. The finer structured pearlitic steels were made by rapidly cooling the steel plate after the hot mill, but strengths were limited to X65.

The next step — microalloyed steels

Microalloyed steels, characterized by a fine microstructure, can reach higher strengths up to X80 and beyond. In order to improve the yield strength, the newer steels had to achieve a finer bainitic structure. This was done by cutting the carbon content by half, which delays the formation of iron carbide and effectively shortens the nose of the CCT diagram. This shortening results in the same cooling rate to produce bainite or martensite rather than pearlite.

The next iteration in the development of microalloyed steels was the addition of small or micro amounts of carbide-forming alloys to "pin" grain boundaries from growing at high austenitic temperatures plus thermo-mechanically rolling the steel at a lower temperature to retain a high dislocation density and a very small grain size after the last pass. Vanadium, niobium/columbium, titanium, rare earths, and boron will only work to pin grain boundaries if the sulphur and oxygen contents are driven very low. Otherwise these expensive alloys disappear in forming larger oxysulphide inclusions in the liquid and are lost to the slag. Once reacted, these expensive alloys are unavailable to pin grain boundaries. This liquid state preparation is done using ladle metallurgy technologies.

These fine microstructures are metastable, and heating causes the dislocations to anneal and the fine precipitates to dissolve, allowing the grains or microstructure to grow and coarsen, resulting in lower strength. Therefore, weld thermal cycles need to be reduced by using lower energy passes that are sequenced to minimize coarsening, temper the previous pass, and extend the time for hydrogen to diffuse out-of-the-weld microstructure. Large weld thermal cycles will severely weaken these modern steel joints.

Improvements by ladle metallurgy

Ladle metallurgy process was designed to first deoxidize and then desulphurize the liquid steel in a basic refractory-lined transfer ladle. Once this deoxidation and desulphurization was achieved, the required microalloy elements were added. The pretreated liquid steel was then transferred to the continuous caster for solidification.

For these higher strength microalloyed steels, the carbon level needs to be further blown down with oxygen to about 0.12% or less. As a result, the levels of oxygen and nitrogen (an oxygen impurity) in solution were much higher when the older pearlitic steel heat was complete and poured from the furnace into the ladle. After the manganese and silicon were added, aluminum was added next. The aluminum removed most of the oxygen. Next magnesium, and sometimes calcium, were added to remove sulphur before adding the grain refining elements. Argon stirring is used to help purge nitrogen and hydrogen from the steel, gather and sweep any solid reaction products or inclusions into the slag, homogenize the alloy content, and avoid temperature stratification rate in the liquid steel heat. These processes were completed before solidification in the continuous caster. Rimming, or gas evolution on solidification in the continuous caster, interferes with solidification, and all the liquid can break out if the solid steel wall is now too thin to hold the internal pressure when the slab exits the water - cooled copper mold.

Inclusion Sizes: Older ingot cast steels contained different families as sizes of inclusions. Pearlitic steels contain the larger sizes. Some formed in the liquid state, which, upon rolling, lead to laminations and possible later mechanical problems. These larger inclusion sizes exceed 500 microns and are typically ladle slag and refractory particles that are easily visible in a cross section. Those between 50 and 200 microns are usually the aluminum oxide or other reaction products such as manganese sulphides or silicates that formed as the steel solidified and were trapped in the iron dendrites. Rolling forms these into long, needle like stringers which decrease the Z direction mechanical properties.

The microalloyed steels, because of the ladle metallurgy, don't normally contain these larger inclusion sizes and are considered much cleaner steels. They do have the smallest inclusions; less than 5 microns in diameter. These inclusions are formed as solid-state reaction products from rare earth or other microalloy elements reacting with the steel impurities forming oxy-nitro-sulphide precipitates. These precipitate from the solid solution in the higher austenitic phase temperatures. These inclusions are needed to pin grain boundaries to ensure the fine grain sizes do not easily grow. The vanadium and niobium/columbium compounds dissolve, going back into solid solution if the temperature is sufficiently high, thereby un-pinning the grain boundaries and lowering the final strength. Titanium inclusions are more stable and more tolerant of higher reheat temperature excursions.

Summary

What does all this mean? As we make progress with increasingly more complicated and interrelated processes, the young engineer should understand the "why" behind these helpful rule of thumb requirements that were placed into standards to avoid known problems and simplify the calculations. Many seemingly simplistic rules have numerous scientific papers, experiments, and years of experience distilled into a few lines of prose or even a coefficient in a calculation. Ask why and consider the physics and chemistry you learned in your background engineering fundamentals.

A simple example: increasing the pipe wall thickness was long known as the practical way to provide inherent protection against both corrosion deterioration and unplanned mechanical damage. Engineers think stress, so the easiest way to add this rule was to require a lower pipe wall stress as the population density (class) increased: i.e. for the same operating pressure, the stress decreases as the wall thickness increases. This was the easiest way to keep things simple.

Consider changes in technology over time and if there are also the changes in material properties to thermal or mechanical forces. Modern steels, unlike pearlitic steels, are metastable and deteriorate if exposed to large thermal cycles. Remember if their yield to ultimate strength ration is high, then the ductility / strain capacity has been consumed to provide strength.

Please think about each job at hand and be aware of the background. Always ask questions. Sometimes the answer lies in two or more places. Both the engineer and the field mechanic must combine observations and experiences to properly understand the phenomenon and start to address a solution.

Pipeline fabrication and construction inspection; preventing bad things before they happen

Bill Amend, P.E.

> *BY GOD, IF I WERE IN CHARGE...*
>
> *There would be improved understanding and implementation of inspection during pipeline construction and maintenance fabrication.*

Introduction

There is an old saying; "you get what you inspect, not what you expect." "Improved" does not necessarily mean "more." However, inspections would be more than a token effort at a one-size-fits-all approach that just allows an operator to check a box on a project "to do list." Inspection work scopes would be developed after assessment of project-specific risks and with recognition of the strengths and limitations of the various inspection options. In forty-years of technical support for pipeline construction, operation, and maintenance, I have witnessed a range of inspection practices ranging from the good, to the bad, to the ugly, and learned from them all. In this chapter, I want to share some of my observations and recommendations.

> *You get what you inspect, not what you expect.*

What is meant by "inspection?"

If you ask three people to define pipeline inspection you are likely to get three different answers. In my experience, it seems that to some people, "pipeline inspection" means nothing more than calling the non-destructive examination (NDE) contractor to come out and radiograph the completed weld and then doing a pressure test. To others, "pipeline inspection" encompasses a multitude of assessments of various pipeline attributes that impact pipeline reliability. For others, the answer is somewhere in between.

In the broadest sense, pipeline inspection can refer to all inspection activities that are undertaken to meet a desired level of quality and reliability. (Some cynics might argue that pipeline inspection is done to meet regulatory requirements, but the regulations generally do attempt to ensure quality and reliability.) Since the desired level of quality and reliability can be different for different pipeline scenarios, the appropriate types of inspections can also be project-specific. By "pipeline scenario," I primarily mean the pipeline-specific, or even the location-specific risk associated with a failure. The scope of an inspection for a small diameter, medium to low-pressure natural gas farm tap in a remote area can be quite different from a large diameter, high-pressure hazardous liquid pipeline located next to a waterway in a highly populated area.

Recall that in the context of pipeline operations, "risk" is generally assessed by considering both the probability of a failure and the consequences of a failure. In turn, consequences can include consideration of:

1. The extent of environmental damage;
2. Injury or death to people;
3. The value of the lost pipeline contents;

4. The value of the lost operation if the failure causes pipeline shutdown, and/or the cost of reduced throughput because of limitations placed on future operations;

5. The cost of the repairs;

6. The potential cost of regulatory fines or penalties;

7. The subjective cost of negative media exposure and the resulting negative effect on public opinion.

Most inspection is geared toward addressing the "probability" portion of the risk assessment by detecting flaws that can cause pipeline failure. However, the types of inspection and thoroughness of the inspection can also impact the consequences. For example, a deep pinhole in a weld and a long seam flaw might both have similar probabilities of causing a release of pipeline product, i.e., a "failure." However, a long flaw in a seam is more likely to have severe consequences than the pinhole because the long axial flaw is more likely to produce a rupture instead of a leak. Therefore, inspection resources that focus on detection of axial flaws could have different benefit than inspections that are optimized for detection of defects that can cause small leaks, even though both features can be classified as "defects."

Our discussion of pipeline inspection needs to consider both the intermediate steps undertaken in the construction and maintenance processes, as well as the finished product. Too often there is complete failure to recognize that inspection of a finished product completely misses the fleeting opportunity to detect and measure characteristics that impact pipeline reliability and the probability of failure. For example, measuring coating dry-film thickness and checking for coating "holidays"* reveals nothing about the quality of the surface preparation. Yet, surface preparation is a key influencing factor on long-term coating performance. For buried or immersed equipment, including pipe-

---

* "Holiday" is a coating industry term for a localized bare spot or related coating discontinuity in a coated surface that leaves the substrate exposed to the corrosive environment. Holidays can also be localized areas in which the coating is present, but the inadequate film thickness makes the discontinuity detectable by some types of holiday detection equipment.

lines, the coating is the first line of defense against corrosion which can cause failure. Radiography or ultrasonic inspection of a weld will confirm absence of rejectable weld flaws, but neither type of nondestructive inspection will confirm that the correct weld metals or heat inputs were used to make the weld. As a result, the mechanical properties of the weld could be different from the design.

I recall a project in which a high-pressure piping system carrying very hot geothermal brine failed because the welders used a stainless-steel welding electrode for the first pass of the weld instead of the specified NiCrMo alloy weld metal that matched the pipe composition. The welds failed from corrosion and stress corrosion cracking, but no inspector was present during the welding to verify the use of the correct weld metal. From the welder's standpoint, the stainless-steel weld metal was much easier to use. The incorrect weld metal was undetectable by radiography.

There is sometimes excessive reliance on pressure testing as a substitute for in-process inspection. I can't recall how many times I have heard the statement, "It passed the hydrotest; it must be OK." Keep in mind that pressure testing typically won't be an effective way of assessing axial strain capacity, but axial strain capacity can be influenced by factors that can be monitored during in-process inspection. Also, a hydrotest may not find flaws that survive the hydrotest, but which grow to failure under the long-term influence of stress cycles that cause fatigue cracking.

Measuring success: How Do You Know When Your Inspection Program Is a Success or a Failure?

Let's consider a deceptively easy question. True or False: If a manufacturing or construction defect is detected after the pipeline is commissioned, your inspection program has failed. Most respondents will answer "True." I believe that the answer is actually "maybe." The answer depends upon the objective of the inspection program. If the objective was to detect all manufacturing and construction defects, then the answer is "True." However, as I will explain below, it is possible that the objectives of the inspection were more limited and that the risks of missing certain types of defects were weighed and the scope of the inspection was adjusted accordingly. If the scope and the performance of the inspection failed to meet the inspection objective, whatever that might be, then the answer would be "True."

If the cost of the inspection program is less than the expected risk of a failure from an undetected defect, then the inspection program could be considered a success. Of course, that weighing of the two costs requires that both the cost of the inspection program and the cost associated with the risk of failure be known with good accuracy. (Remember, the risk considers both the probability and the consequence of a failure.) It is the classic "garbage in/garbage out" situation. The cost of the inspection cannot be justified if the cost associated with the risk of an abbreviated inspection is not known. It is not common for the staff who develop the inspection protocol to be the same as the staff who assess the risk of failure and the associated costs. As a result, there often is some teamwork involved in developing cost-effective inspection protocols.

Let's assume that the risk of a failure has been accurately assessed and you are responsible for developing the inspection scope and inspection procedures. We can now look at the considerations in developing an optimized inspection program.

Developing an inspection program

For the purposes of this section, let's assume that the reader is responsible for developing a project-specific inspection protocol and defining the resources needed to perform that protocol. The inspection program can consist of five steps. Each is summarized in Figure 1. Further below I discuss how those steps can be achieved.

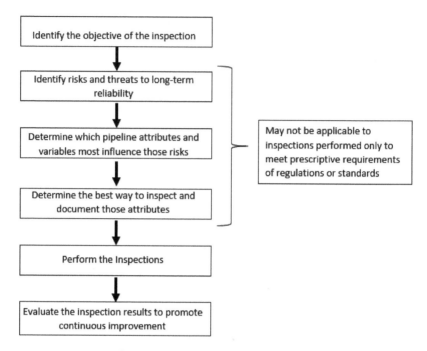

Figure 1. High-level summary of the inspection process.

The first step is defining the objective of the inspection. Options include various combinations of the following five considerations. Each of the five can be weighted in different ways for different projects, although, in my experience, the five options are listed in order of how they are often prioritized, with regulatory compliance being a top priority.

1. **Compliance with applicable regulatory requirements:** For example, many pipelines are subject to the requirements of 49 CFR Parts 192 or 195. The regulatory requirements are baseline requirements. Failure to meet them can result in economic penalties, even if an objective assessment could conclude that the failure to meet the details of the requirements did not result in any increased risk. Regulators will generally tell you that regulations are baselines and that compliance with regulations alone will not always ensure safe and reliable operation. Reg-

ulators will typically expect you to go further than the baseline represented by the regulations.

2. **Compliance with applicable Company specifications, procedures and standards:** Examples include the content of the company design standards or operations and maintenance (O&M) manual. Some regulatory jurisdictions consider company procedures to be as enforceable and auditable as the regulatory standards themselves. Failure to meet these could also result in economic penalties. Authors of the company standards must walk a fine line between providing enough guidance to users while retaining some flexibility to accommodate specific circumstances. Overly prescriptive procedures can restrict the company from using cost effective, technically prudent options that work well in some circumstances. For example, the statement that, "Company ABC welding practices and weld inspections will comply with all requirements of API 1104 Welding of Pipelines and Related Facilities," is easy to make and it sounds great. However, it usually (inadvertently) results in the following:

   a. Fails to recognize that not all parts of API 1104 are required to be followed in order to meet the requirements of the federal pipeline safety regulations;

   b. possibly results in the wrong standard being applied to some welds. For example, using Section IX of the ASME Boiler and Pressure Vessel Code may be required for some welds referenced in some sections of the ASME B31 code; and,

   c. prevents the use of new technically defensible welding and inspection practices since the delay time between development of new technology and the incorporation into API 1104 (or any other consensus standard) can take several years.

3. **Compliance with applicable industry consensus standards**: Examples include API Standard 1104, ASME B31.3, or NACE MR-01-75. Sometimes portions of these are directly referenced by the regulatory standards and become "requirements." Often, they serve as helpful resources for the development of company standards and procedures, but typically they are not enough to optimize a response to every circumstance that can be encountered in the construction and maintenance processes.

4. **Compliance with other best practices that are applicable to project-specific or site-specific conditions or integrity threats**. This is where subject matter experts (SMEs), either within the company or in the form of contractors, consultants or service providers, can be valuable resources. This is also why company standards need to be flexible enough to accommodate the project-specific recommendations of the SME.

5. **Enabling continuous improvement in the construction or maintenance activity by providing a record of what went right, what went wrong, and the root cause of *why* it went wrong**. If a pipeline fails, or if inspection reject rates become alarmingly high, detailed inspection records can help get to the root cause of the problem so that future inspections and quality assurance protocols can be adjusted accordingly. It is one thing to know that four cracks were discovered in the root passes of a population of 50 girth welds. It is more useful to also know that a) the four welds which cracked were not among those randomly selected for monitoring of heat input by the weld inspector, b) that they were among those completed using the lowest weld heat input or, c) that they had the longest time between completion of the weld root pass and the start of the subsequent weld passes. Any of those three potential causes in my hypothetical example can influence the way future projects are performed and inspected.

Once the objectives are clearly defined, the next step is to develop the inspection details to ensure that the objectives are achieved. That means consideration of:

1. What will be inspected or monitored?

I always found it easier to start with a comprehensive list of potential inspection topics and whittle it down to fit the specific needs of the project than to start with a blank piece of paper. An outstanding resource for that comprehensive list is a Quality Management System (QMS) document. PHMSA sponsored development of one specifically for pipeline construction projects. The report "Improving Quality Management Systems (QMS) for Pipeline Construction Activities" is accessible for free here: https://primis.phmsa.dot.gov/matrix/PrjHome.rdm?prj=504. It includes separate tables for 22 distinct construction activities. Each table describes the quality concerns, the inspection requirements, and the training and competency of inspection personnel applicable to that activity. API 1177, "Recommended Practice for Steel Pipeline Construction Quality Management Systems," is a similar resource.

The answer to the question of what to inspect can also be guided through careful review of the specification. We can assume that the specification details the important attributes of each intermediate step in the construction or maintenance process, as well as describing the acceptable conditions of the finished product. However, not all the requirements in a specification have equal impact on reliability. While all the variables in a specification must be met to claim conformance to "the spec," the specification my not provide much help in prioritizing which variables deserve the most attention from the standpoint of long-term reliability and quality. Long term reliability and quality is not necessarily a one-to-one match with what is required to meet the specification.

Here is an example from pipeline welding. The standard's guiding content of welding procedure specifications generally require that the current, voltage, and travel speed ranges be specified. Those three variables are all considered in calculating the heat input for the weld. From a metallurgical standpoint, we know that the heat input of the weld has the largest influence on mechanical properties. Individual values of current, voltage, and travel speed play minor roles as long as the calculated or measured heat input value is within the desired range. I am much more interested in the extent to which the heat inputs are optimized than I am in making sure the voltage does not deviate from the specified range by a single volt.

Furthermore, heat input is much easier to measure than arc voltage. When I did welding inspection training, I used to show a brief video of a voltmeter readout when it was connected to an arc welding circuit. The class members would watch the 6-second video and write down what they judged the average voltage to be. The answers were as numerous as the attendees because the voltage varies, and the displayed values change rapidly. In contrast, simple measurements of deposited weld-bead length and length of burned-off welding electrodes are enough to estimate the average heat input if the electrode diameter is known. Measurements of length using a tape measure result in far less variation among different inspectors than the interpretation of voltmeter measurements. Therefore, it again comes down to the objective of the inspection. Are we trying to show strict compliance to the details of a specification (quantitative voltage measurement) or are we trying to show high likelihood of good reliability and performance (heat input)?

2. What percentage of observable or measurable activities or deliverables will be inspected?

This is a more difficult question. It is seldom possible to inspect everything. For example, a single inspector cannot monitor all weld passes on all welds during pipeline construction. There are too many welding activities occurring simultaneously. We must prioritize the risks associated with each part of the construction process and focus resources where they are most effective. Using weld inspection as an example, experience from past welding projects and the long-term performance of those completed pipelines can guide our allocation of welding inspection efforts and resources.

The percentage of features being inspected should be a moving target. If deficiencies are found in inspections of randomly selected samples for one attribute or variable, then more samples should be inspected. An example of a simplistic approach that I have seen used is that for each out-of-specification measurement, two additional measurements of the same type will be made.

There are more statistically defensible methods for developing sampling plans. One example is the sequential probability ratio test (SPRT)*. In a SPRT, the number of inspections to be made varies and is based on both the selected reliability target and the results of the initial inspections. The SPRT basically sets a minimum number of inspections and a threshold ratio of "accept" to "reject" inspection results. The SPRT results are graphically represented as shown in the example in Figure 2. The inspections continue until two conditions are both met:

a. The number of inspections exceeds the minimum calculated requirement; and,

b. Either the population "accept" line or population "reject" threshold line is crossed

In the illustrated example, a total of 30 inspections were made and 10 unacceptable results were obtained. However, for the selected reliability target, which controls the positions and slopes of the diagonal red and green lines, we could have concluded after only 15 inspections that the population of samples would not meet the reliability target. The inspections could have stopped after 15 inspections and the population of samples rejected.

Both approaches (statistically based, or, inspect "x" more for each "reject") are different from an inflexible target of inspecting XX% of all occurrences of the attribute, regardless of findings.

---

*   For example, see W.V. Harper, D.J. Stucki, T.M. Shie, R.J. Davis, "Reliability Based Facility Risk Assessment," ASME International Pipeline Conference IPC2010-31352.

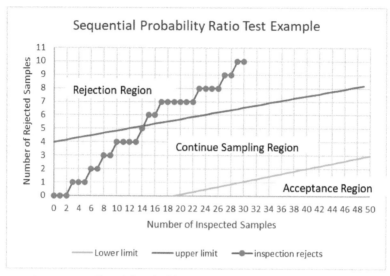

Figure 2. Example of the sequential probability ratio test

Inspections performed after the blue line crosses the red line or the green line are unnecessary; the desired reliability target will have either been met (green line) or not (red line).

3. What human resources will be needed to accomplish the inspections?

Clearly, the human resources needed will be influenced by the scope of the inspections to be performed. Different inspectors have different skills, experience and expertise. That is true even within subsets of inspectors. Using welding inspectors as an example, some welding inspectors used to be pipeline welders. Others were never welders. Some have gone through the various certification programs such as the AWS Certified Welding Inspector (AWS CWI) or the National Welding Inspection School Certified Pipeline Welding Inspector (CPWI) programs. Others are highly competent inspectors who never were welders and who never took the certification tests, but who are highly familiar with the intricacies of the production process and deliverable they are responsible for inspecting. So, who to pick?

In my experience, an inspector who used to be a craftsman has a great understanding of the issues that can interfere with the ability to do the job well, and how less scrupulous craftsmen can take short cuts. They might be well suited to make specific suggestions to the craftsman to improve quality. However, performing the work and inspecting the work are related, but not the same. The inspector needs separate training on using the inspection instruments and doing the documentation. The inspector can also require different communication skills than the craftsman.

On the other hand, someone with an inspection qualification certificate should know how to use the instruments and have some familiarity with the applicable standards, but they may have never been in a pipeline right-of-way before. Even worse, the inspector may never have been trained to apply the inspection methods to pipelines. For example, an AWS CWI could have taken the test for structural welding according to AWD D1.1 requirements, instead of to the requirements of API 1104. An AWS CWI might never have seen a copy of API 1104, much less studied it. Translating book knowledge or classroom learning into effective inspection practices is not as easy as it sounds. Those inspectors would surely benefit by acting as an apprentice inspector or a helper to a senior inspector in the real-world conditions of a pipeline construction project.

4. What equipment, tools, or instruments will be needed to support the inspections?

This gets to the question of how the critical variables will be measured. Few inspections can be performed using only the inspector's eyes. However, I have been on projects where the so-called "welding inspector" had minimal training, and no way of measuring current or voltage or heat input or joint-fit-up or finished weld dimensions. That is not "inspection." That is just witnessing.

Selection of tools and instruments will be guided by the types of variables or attributes to be measured, just as those are, in turn, guided by the content of the specification and the objective of the inspection.

Many times, there is more than one way of doing a measurement and the method can influence the result. I already mentioned the difficulty in measuring welding arc voltage. There are different types of instrumentation such as purpose-built data recorders that make determination of average values much less subjective than using a generic voltmeter. Similarly, *where* the measurement is made can also influence results. Using the example of welding inspection again, a voltage measurement at the welding machine connections will produce a different value than voltage measured close to the arc. For consistency, when more than one method of measurement is available, the acceptable methods should be specified in the procedure to prevent apples-to-oranges comparisons of results.

5. **What reporting relationships and levels of authority will the inspectors have with other project staff?**

This one is deceptively important. Everyone who interacts with the inspector needs to know what level of authority the inspector has been granted by the project management. Is the inspector only an advisor to the project manager? Can the inspector require that the craftsmen change the way they do their tasks? Can the inspector shut down the job until changes are made? Basically, a key question is whether the inspector is an observer or an enforcer. The biggest problems occur when the craftsmen and contractors believe the inspector's authority is different from what the inspector thinks. Everyone needs to have the same understanding when the project starts.

6. **What level of detail will be used in the documentation process?**

There are many options, so I have dedicated the entire next section to documentation.

Documentation options

Documentation is the permanent record of the inspection. It serves to verify that the finished product meets specification. However, it can do more than that. Inspection documentation can be useful for trending so that adjustments are made to the construction process before rejections occur. Inspection documentation can be a valuable input to the process of continuous improvement. Inspection documentation can also be a valuable tool to support root cause analysis in the future if an in-service failure occurs.

We have probably all seen it: an inspection form is produced for a localized pipeline repair and the same form is used for the installation of 50-miles of new high-pressure pipe in a virgin ROW, even though the scope of work is entirely different. Just as the scope of construction or maintenance work can be different, the scope of the inspection can be much different, and therefore the documentation also needs to be different. There are, however, some minimum requirements for documentation of inspections. In my opinion, every inspection record, regardless of the kind of item or activity being inspected, should include at least the following information:

Key Inspection Record Content

- Inspector name
- Identification number or unique location of the inspected item, or description of the inspected activity
- Inspection method(s) or instruments used, and, if applicable, the inspection procedure name/number used

- Inspection date
- Number or name of the reference specification used for accept/reject criteria
- Measured data or other inspection results
- Conclusion: "accept" or "reject"

In addition to the minimum requirements applicable to all inspections, the documentation will also include entries specific to the type of inspection being performed. Those entries could be considered subsets of the "measured data or other inspection results" listed in the box above and generally represent the majority of the inspection documentation.

In my experience there are three different types of inspection documentation fields, each of which can be used alone or in combination with the others. Each has some advantages and limitations.

1. **Binary:** This is the simple "Accept"/"Reject" or "Yes"/"No" input. Short. Simple. Easy. There are only two boxes from which to choose; merely check the appropriate box. However, it has little value other than to confirm that the performed task and the final product met the specification (or not). It has little value if the goal is continuous improvement or for root cause analysis of failure to meet the specification. Examples of where binary responses can be acceptable for a hypothetical welding project include, but may not be limited to, the following:

    a. Welder qualification documentation acceptable?
    b. Welding procedure specification (WPS) on site?
    c. Pipe and fitting size matches specification?
    d. Pipe grade on pipe matches specification?
    e. Welding process matches the WPS?
    f. Electrode type matches the WPS and project specification (example: AWS A5.5 E8018 A1)?
    g. Electrodes taken from hermetically sealed container per project specification?

2. **Gradient or quantitative**: This format requires the inspector to further describe his observations or measurements. For example, the angle was not just acceptable, it was 45° +/- 2°. The coating dry-film thickness was 17-mils minimum and 20-mils maximum with an average of 18.2-mils for 20 measurements. The welding heat input was not just within the specified range of 27-kJ/in or greater, it was 28-33-kJ/in for the fill passes. This type of quantitative data supports trending and statistical analysis in addition to providing a basis for judging whether the specification was met.

3. **Free form or narrative**: This is where the inspector records subjective observations that can be useful for root cause analyses. The inspection "form" may be little more than a blank sheet with some prompts included that give the inspector guidance on what types of observations to record, but not necessarily how to record them. This format is also used sometimes when more specific inspection forms are not provided. Example entries could include, "Joint fit-up for welding was adversely affected by rough handling of the pipe when unloaded from the trucks by contractor ABC. End protectors for several of the pipes were missing or torn upon delivery." Other examples include: "The second weld pass on weld #8 was delayed for a few minutes while shoring was adjusted to improve the stability of the excavation. The longest observed delay time was 9 minutes. Second passes of most welds were started within 3 minutes." "The majority of the thinnest areas of coating were at the 6 o'clock position," or, "After joint #12 was coated, tarps were erected prior to spray coating to minimize contamination of surface prep by windblown dirt."

While narrative documentation puts the reader in the shoes of the inspector, it can be difficult to use for trending and does not support quantitative analysis of the data unless quantitative measurements are included in the narrative.

Besides consideration of the input field type, the inspection project manager needs to decide if the paper or electronic record is best. Paper documentation worked for many decades, but the transfer of information from remote locations to the home office or construction management trailer only occurs as fast as the paper can be forwarded. New electronic options, such as tablets, allow data to be recorded, automatically checked for conformance to the specification, and shared almost instantaneously with others via Wi-Fi or cellular connections. With built-in alarms or alerts, an inspector can be less familiar with the detailed requirements of the specification because the device can be set-up to automatically compare entries against the requirements. In addition, some systems automatically record the GPS position at which the data entry is made and apply a time stamp to entry. Bar code stickers can be applied to features to be inspected. When coupled with tablets that incorporate bar code scanners the bar codes facilitate fast and accurate transcription of the sample identification and related details into the inspector's report (Figure 3).

While electronic forms can be set up to do automatic quality assurance checks on the data entries, paper forms cannot. Therefore, when using paper forms one challenge is to ensure that the inspector is fully aware of the specification requirements or the benchmarks for comparison of quantitative measurements.

Figure 3. Bar code scanning into a tablet and portion of a related weld inspection record showing weld number, GPS location and inspection status summary (images courtesy of Metegrity Inc.)

I favor a three-column format. The first column is the type of measurement or observation required. For example, "weld voltage for the cap pass," or "coating dry film thickness." The second column is the acceptable range of measurements. In the case of the weld cap pass, the acceptable values from the specification might be "24-32 volts." In the third column is the inspector's measurement made during the inspection. Comparing data in column 3 to the acceptable range summarized in column 2 facilitates easy identification of conformance versus non-conformance. Sometimes I have given the inspector the specification and the form with column two not yet populated. The inspector is then required to read the entire specification and fill out column two before starting the inspections. It is one way of forcing the inspector to read the specification.

There are a few guidelines that are equally applicable to all the documentation types. If the inspector relies on inputs from anyone else, then the inspector should note who provided those inputs. Ideally, that other person would sign or initial the portion of the document that includes their observations to indicate that the information was accurately transcribed by the inspector. In the case of supporting non-destructive inspections performed by another party (example: radiographic inspection by an NDT contractor) the inspector should record the NDT report number and names of NDT contractor and inspectors on his report.

The inspector

Up to now we have been discussing the development of the inspection scope and procedures. Now let's look at the role of the human resources, i.e., the inspector, in more detail. The inspector makes or breaks the inspection program. I break down the key attributes and functions of an inspector into the acronym LEDR, i.e., "be a LEDR." Spelled out, it stands for "Learn," "Evaluate," "Document," "Report."

Learn: There are multiple facets to this part. The inspector needs the applicable job skills. The job skills include; a) having thorough knowledge and understanding of the applicable specifications, b) having necessary technical competency to use the inspection tools, c) making and documenting the required observations and measurements in the prescribed manner, and d) having the communication skills necessary to interface with everyone on the job site including craftsmen and project managers.

Some communication skills might be somewhat intuitive, but the ability to communicate effectively across multiple levels of project authority is also a learned skill that is not often covered adequately in training courses and certification programs. That is especially true when it comes to inspection tasks that require you to get "in the space" of various craftsmen who often see the inspector as a hindrance or worse, an adversary.

Sometimes the communication is nonverbal. One of my first tasks with a new company was to do the inspection and documentation related to the qualification testing of a new welding procedure. I was the "new guy" as far as the welders were concerned, even if I was a senior level engineer. At the conclusion of the welding, I grabbed a broom and helped clean up. The welders said they had never seen an engineer work a broom before. By that action, though, they understood we were basically on the same team and chasing the same goals, we just had different titles and roles in the project.

The second skill, not often covered well in formal training courses, is the ability to use observations and data to get to a root cause of a failure to meet a specification. Sometimes the responsibility for the root cause analysis is delegated to others in the project staff. However, the inputs of the inspectors who find the deviations are valuable inputs. The ability to put the pieces of the puzzle together and to detect patterns associated with repeated deviations from the specification make the inspector a more valuable member of the team. Working alongside other, more experienced and respected inspectors, and mimicking their practices, can be a fast track to becoming more skilled and respected yourself.

Evaluate: This is the primary function. The inspector must be able to apply his learned skills to make the specified observations and measurements. Then, and equally as import, the inspector makes the judgement of whether the observed condition meets the specification or not.

Document: The old saying is that, "No job is finished until the paperwork is compete." The saying applies well to inspection. These days "paperwork" might mean data entry into a tablet or other handheld device. Most of the time the format for inspection documentation will be dictated by company procedure or by the staff who develop the documentation format for the project. Some of the options for documentation format and options for the level of documentation detail have been described elsewhere in this chapter.

Report: By "report," I mean make sure the appropriate staff know when deviations from the specification are detected. (This gets back to the earlier discussion in this chapter that describes the level of authority given to inspectors and the importance of clearly defining the reporting relationships to project management.) At first, this does not seem to be an obvious step in the process. After all, we have already mentioned the importance of documentation. However, an example from a real project illustrates how the inspection process should not stop at documentation.

Welders were being qualified to work on a new pipeline project. The company diligently assigned inspectors to monitor the welders as they made their test welds prior to the start of production welding. Welders are required to follow the details of the applicable qualified welding procedure specification when they make the test weld. The inspectors recorded all the important variables (current, voltage, travel speed, etc.) and the welds were tested successfully in accordance with API 1104. The process stopped at that point. The welders were now supposedly "qualified" because their test welds passed the required mechanical tests and had no rejectable flaws. The welders then made many production welds during pipeline construction.

PHMSA auditors then visited the pipeline construction site and did their customary check of construction practices and the qualifications of the welders. It was at that point that they discovered by review of the inspector records that some of the welders had welded outside of the specified range of some of the welding variables in the welding procedure specification when they took their qualification tests. Therefore, the welders were technically not "qualified," even though their production welds passed radiographic inspection.

The inspectors had documented the welding variables during the welder qualification testing but had not told anyone that the recorded variables were outside the specified range. The company project management staff had not reviewed the inspection documents in enough detail to catch the deviations; the focus was on whether the test welds passed the required destructive and nondestructive tests. As a result, the production welds were declared by PHMSA to have not been made by qualified welders and a very large fine was imposed on the company. In addition, PHMSA required extensive destructive and nondestructive testing of several examples of the production welds that had been made by those welders to "prove" that the welds made by those welders were acceptable.

The bottom line is that when deviations from the specification are observed, they need to not only be documented, but the appropriate people need to know in a timely manner.

Summary

Inspection of pipeline construction and fabrication can mean a lot of things. *Effective* pipeline inspection means a multiple step process that can include some or all the following steps, depending upon the objectives:

- Identifying the real objective of the inspection, i.e., just meeting regulations versus optimizing reliability and performance;
- Identifying the applicable risks and threats to long-term safe and efficient operation;
- Determining what pipeline attributes minimize those risks and prioritizing those attributes for inspection;
- Determining how to best inspect for and document those attributes; and

- Evaluating the inspection results to facilitate root cause analysis of deviations and to promote continuous improvement of the construction or fabrication process.

The keys to success include getting the right inspection resources (people and tools), giving the inspection staff clearly defined authority, and learning from the inspection results to make the next project even more successful.

Authors' contact information

Bill Amend
 Email: billamend4plmetallurgy@yahoo.com

Dr. Bill Bruce
 Email: bill.bruce@dnvgl.com
 Phone: 614-734-6128
 Web address: www.dnvgl.com

Geoff Foreman
 Email: geoff_foreman@shaw.ca

Mike Gloven
 Email: michaelgloven@expertinfrasolutions.com
 Phone: 303-881-4379
 Web address: www.expertinfrasolutions.com

Dave Johnson
 Email: David.johnson@energytransfer.com

Shawn Laughlin
 Email: slaughlin@laughlincompanies.net
 Phone: 281-900-7029
 Web address: www.pipespring.net

Dr. Keith Leewis
 Email: Keith@Leewis.US
 Phone: 713.376.9499

Dr. Brian Leis
 Email: bleis@columbus.rr.com;

Jane Rau

Email: jane.rau@jtrain-inc.com

Phone: 713-446-6329

Web address: www.jtrain-inc.com

Jerry Rau

Email: Jerry.rau@jtrain-inc.com

Phone: 713-204-4380

Web address: www.jtrain-inc.com

George Tenley

Email: myhusli@gmail.com

Phone: 301-922-3773 (cell)

304-754-3609 (home)